Revision Q[uide] for Intermediate 2 Chemistry

D A Buchanan
(Moray House Institute,
Edinburgh University)

J R Melrose
(Lenzie Academy,
Lenzie, Glasgow)

Assisted by

J M Briggs
(Dalziel High School,
Motherwell)

Published by
Chemcord
Inch Keith
East Kilbride
Glasgow

ISBN   1 870570 70 7

© Buchanan and Melrose, 1999
First reprint 2003

Typeset by J M Briggs
Printed by Bell and Bain Ltd, Glasgow

Contents

Note to teachers and lecturers

The exercises are specifically written to test students' understanding of the key ideas in the Intermediate 2 Chemistry (Higher Still) course and to give students practice in the kinds of questions used in the examinations. They have been trialled over a number of years and found to be an invaluable revision aid.

The exercises are, by and large, independent of each other and consequently they can be used to fit almost any teaching order. They can be used in a variety of situations, e.g. self-study time in school or homework.

The variation in the length of the exercises is a reflection of the different kinds of questions which are associated with a particular part of the course. Teachers / lecturers may wish to focus on areas which are known to be difficult for their students.

A book of answers to the revision questions is also available.

Acknowledgement

A number of the questions in the exercises come from or have evolved from questions used in the SCE examinations. The publisher wishes to thank the Scottish Qualifications Authority for permission to use examination questions in these ways.

Unit 1
Exercise 1.1

Elements

1. Name **two** elements which are
   (a) metallic,
   (b) non-metallic,
   (c) solid at room temperature,
   (d) liquid at room temperature,
   (e) gas at room temperature,
   (f) naturally-occurring as compounds,
   (g) naturally occurring as elements,
   (h) made in the lab by scientists.

2. The elements are arranged in the Periodic Table.
   (a) Approximately how many different elements exist?
   (b) Explain what is meant by
       (i) a group,
       (ii) a period.

3. (a) Name the elements with each of the following symbols.
       (i) V   (ii) Li   (iii) Ar   (iv) Ni
       (v) Cl   (vi) K   (vii) Ne   (viii) F
   (b) From the list above, name the elements which are members of each of the following families.
       (i) the halogens   (ii) the alkali metals
       (iii) the transition metals   (iv) the noble gases
   (c) State a chemical property of
       (i) the alkali metals,   (ii) the noble gases.

4. (a) Write the symbol for each of the following elements.
       (i) sodium   (ii) helium   (iii) aluminium
       (iv) carbon   (v) lead   (vi) gallium
   (b) Which **two** of the above elements will have similar chemical properties?

5. Germanium is so similar to silicon that it was once called "eka silicon".
   Why are germanium and silicon chemically similar to each other?

6. Write the name and symbol of an element which is
   (a) stored under oil,
   (b) stored under water,
   (c) used in swimming pools,
   (d) used as lead in pencils,
   (e) used as the metal in domestic light bulbs,
   (f) used as the gas in domestic light bulbs,
   (g) once used to fill airships,
   (h) now used in lighter than air balloons,
   (i) makes up approx. 80% of the air,
   (j) makes up approx. 20% of the air,
   (k) called after a planet,
   (l) called after a continent,
   (m) called after an American state,
   (n) called after Albert Einstein,
   (o) called after the man who discovered dynamite,
   (p) called after the woman who discovered radium.

Exercise 1.2   Compounds and mixtures

1. (a) Explain what is meant by
        (i) an element,   (ii) a compound.
    (b) Explain whether or not it is possible to make different substances by
        breaking up
        (i) an element,   (ii) a compound.
    (c) Look at the following list of substances:

        iron, sodium sulphite, carbon, oxygen, sugar,
        salt, copper chloride, magnesium

        Which can be broken up to make different substances?

2. Divide the following list of substances into elements and compounds:

    carbon, petrol, alcohol, zinc, oxygen, sugar, sodium chloride,
    gold, copper sulphate, nitrogen, aluminium, silver oxide

3. Read the passage below carefully.

    > Oxygen is involved in many everyday reactions.
    >
    > Glucose is a compound containing carbon, hydrogen and oxygen. It is
    > built up in plants from carbon dioxide and water in a process called
    > photosynthesis. Oxygen is released in the reaction.
    >
    > The starch in our food is broken down to form glucose.
    > During respiration, glucose and oxygen react and energy is produced
    > in the process.
    >
    > The reaction of oxygen with coal and gas releases energy which can
    > be used as a source of heat in our houses. In a car engine, petrol
    > combines with oxygen in another energy-producing reaction.
    >
    > Oxygen, as well as water, is involved in the rusting iron - a reaction
    > which costs this country many millions of pounds each year. The iron
    > can be protected by coating the surface with zinc, copper or gold.

    Make a table to show all the elements and compounds mentioned in the passage.

4. (a) Name the compound which is formed when each of the following pairs of
        elements join up.
        (i) magnesium and chlorine   (ii) lead and sulphur
        (iii) sodium and oxygen   (iv) hydrogen and iodine
    (b) Name **two** possible compounds containing potassium, sulphur and
        oxygen.

5. (a) A colourless gas **W** relights a glowing splint;
        W reacts with magnesium to form a white powder **X**;
        W reacts with a black solid **Y** to form carbon dioxide.
        Name the substances **W**, **X** and **Y**.
    (b) Why does air **not** relight a glowing splint?

6. Copy the list of substances and complete all the columns.
    (One example is already done for you.)

Formula of substance	Element	Compound	Elements present
CaSO$_3$	No	Yes	calcium, sulphur, oxygen
He			
NaBr			
LiCl			
ZnI$_2$			
Fe			
KNO$_3$			
Xe			
I$_2$			
BaSO$_4$			
Sn			
HCl			
Hg			
As			
MgCO$_3$			

7. When iron and sulphur are mixed and heated in a test tube until the mixture
    glows red, the iron cannot be separated from the sulphur using a magnet.
    (a) What name is given to substances like iron and sulphur which contain only
         one kind of atom?
    (b) Why can the iron **not** be separated from the sulphur after heating?

8. Crude oil is a mixture of compounds.
    (a) Explain what is meant by a mixture.
    (b) Consider the following list of substances:

                 air, iron, oxygen, water, milk, soil, carbon dioxide

         Make a table showing
         (i)   the substances which are mixtures,
         (ii) the substances which are pure.

9. (a) Explain what is meant by
        (i) a solute,   (ii) a solvent,
        (iii) a saturated solution.
   (b) Household vinegar is made by dissolving ethanoic acid in water.
       Name
        (i) the solute,   (ii) the solvent,
        (iii) the solution.
   (c) Draw diagrams to show the difference between a dilute solution and a
       concentrated solution.

10. State symbols are used with symbols and formulae to label elements and
    compounds.

CCl$_4$(l)   HCl(aq)   S(s)   CO$_2$(g)

    Construct a table to give the meaning of the state symbols shown.

11. A substance **X** was heated as shown.

substance X   glowing splint relights

heat

   (a) Which gas is produced when **X** is heated?
   (b) From this experiment, what can be learned about **X**?

12. A pupil wanted to investigate whether a paint absorbs air when it dries. The apparatus shown below was used.

syringe   syringe

**glass slides covered
in wet gloss paint**

At the start of the experiment, the total volume of air inside the apparatus was 100 cm³. Every day the air in the apparatus was passed back and forth over the painted glass slides. The remaining volume of gas in the apparatus was measured. The results are shown in the graph below.

(a) (i) Name the gas which is most likely to have reacted with the paint.

    (ii) Explain your answer.

(b) This paint is normally dry to the touch after 1 day.

    In this experiment, the paint was still sticky after 1 day.

    Suggest a reason for this difference.

13. Some bags of potato crisps are filled with pure nitrogen gas instead of air.

    Suggest why this is done.

14. Chlorine is used in a wide range of chemicals.

    More chlorine (27%) is used to make the plastic PVC than for any other use.

    Solvents for dry cleaning and paints require 16% of the chlorine produced.

    17% is used for making aerosol propellants.

    Chemical reactions making, for example, hydrochloric acid and bleach, account for 14% of the chlorine used.

    Other uses include the making of disinfectants, anaesthetics and insecticides (26%).

    Construct a table with **two** headings to show this information.

15. Black and white photographic papers can be made with different proportions of silver compounds.

There are three types. Here are their names and compositions.

bromide   (100% silver bromide)

bromo-chloride   (60% silver bromide, 40% silver chloride)

chloro-bromide   (60% silver chloride, 40% silver bromide)

Some examples of papers are:

Brovira and Pal - bromide papers

Galerie, Oriental and Elite - bromo-chloride

Record-Rapid and Portriga - chloro-bromide type

Choose suitable headings and present the information about black and white photographic papers in the form of a table.

16. Arctic seas support more life than might be expected. This is mainly due to the greater availability of dissolved oxygen in the colder water.

The table shows the relationship between the temperature of the water and the amount of dissolved oxygen.

Temperature of water / °C	0	20	40	60	70	80
Concentration of dissolved oxygen / grams in each cubic metre	69.4	43.4	30.8	22.7	18.6	13.8

(a) Draw a **line graph** to show these results.

(b) The average temperature of the seas around Scotland is approximately 9°C. Give the concentration of oxygen available at this temperature.

(c) Give the temperature of the water which contains 25 g of dissolved oxygen in each cubic metre.

17.

A lemonade bottle was made by heating 200 g of sand with 150 g of sodium carbonate and 50 g of calcium carbonate.

(a) Present this information as a table.

(b) Present this information in another suitable way.

18. Copper(II) sulphate solution is blue. When it is placed in a beam of light, some light is absorbed and some passes through.

David investigated this effect to see if the amount of light passing through depends on the concentration of the copper(II) sulphate solution.

He obtained the following results.

Concentration of $CuSO_4$ / moles per litre	0.05	0.2	0.4	0.6	0.8	1.0
Light passing through / %	74.0	29.0	11.0	5.0	3.0	2.0

(a) Draw a **line graph** to show these results.

(b) State the relationship between the amount of light passing through and the concentration of the copper(II) sulphate solution.

(c) Use your graph to estimate the concentration of a copper(II) sulphate solution which allows 50% of the light to pass through.

19. The flowchart shows some of the many chemicals obtained from wood.

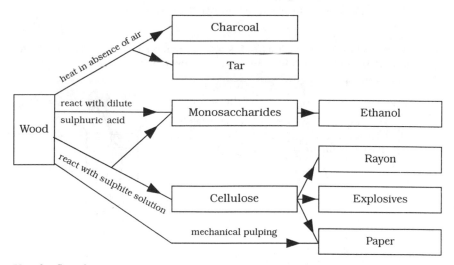

Use the flowchart to

(a) name the compound which is made from wood and used to make rayon.

(b) name the type of **chemical** treatment of wood that is the first stage in paper making.

Exercise 1.3   Chemical reactions

1. (a) Explain what is meant by a chemical reaction.
   (b) Which of the following refer to a chemical reaction?
   - (i)   frying an egg
   - (ii) a puddle of water evaporating
   - (iii) salt dissolving in water
   - (iv) the burning of petrol
   - (v) the melting of a plastic
   - (vi) nitrogen combining with hydrogen
   - (vii) wool growing on a sheep
   - (viii) the breaking of glass
   - (ix) the rotting of compost
   - (x) separating alcohol from water
   - (xi) heating a metal
   - (xii) separating sand from water

2. In each of the following reactions, what might be seen that shows that a chemical reaction is taking place?
   - (a) sodium reacting with chlorine to form sodium chloride
   - (b) the burning of coal
   - (c) magnesium reacting with dilute acid to form hydrogen

3. (a) Explain what is meant by an **exothermic** reaction.
   (b) Explain what is meant by an **endothermic** reaction.

4. On Andy's first day in chemistry his teacher demonstrated an experiment to the class. Here is the report that Andy wrote in his notebook.

> Mr. Murray took this really thin kind of copper and put it in a jar of gas. The gas was chlorine. We had to keep clear of the chlorine he said.
> When the copper went in the gas, it shrivelled up. Then it went on fire. When it stopped there was yellow stuff in the jar. This is a CHEMICAL REACTION.

copper

chlorine

   (a) From Andy's report give **two** pieces of evidence which suggest that a chemical reaction had taken place.
   (b) Name the compound formed in this reaction.

5. "Handwarmers" are intended for use by people who spend time in cold conditions.

    They consist of an outer packet made of strong plastic plus metal foil.

    The packet contains colourless crystals and a weak inner bag which is full of a grey powder.

    When the packet is rubbed between the hands, the inner bag breaks open and its contents mix with the crystals.

    The packet can then be placed in a pocket or glove to keep the hands warm for a period of time.

    If the packet is opened after being used it is found to contain only a black powder.

    Suggest **two** pieces of evidence from the passage to support the idea that handwarmers work by means of a chemical reaction.

Exercise 1.4   Factors affecting reaction rate

1. List the following in order of rate of reaction, fastest first:
    milk turning sour,   an egg frying,   a motor car rusting,   a match igniting

2. The speed of a reaction depends on the reaction conditions.
    Describe how each of the following affects the speed of a reaction.
    (a) particle size of the reactants
    (b) concentration of the reactants
    (c) temperature of the reactants
    (d) using a catalyst

3. Three experiments are set up as shown. Each experiment is carried out at room temperature and the mass of magnesium is the same in each case.

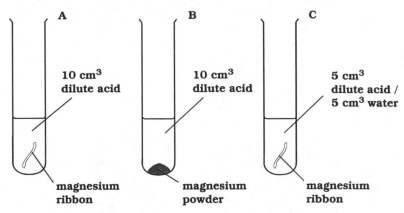

    (a) Explain any difference that would be observed between
         (i)   **A** and **B**,
         (ii) **A** and **C**.
    (b) Explain any difference that would be observed if experiment **A** was repeated at 50 °C.

4. Natural gas will burn in a bunsen burner.
    (a) What happens to the temperature of the flame when the air hole is opened.
    (b) Explain your answer.

5. Different chemical reactions happen at different speeds.
    Give an example of an everyday reaction which
    (a) is finished after a few seconds,
    (b) takes between a few minutes and a few hours to be finished,
    (c) goes on for many years.

6. A jet of petrol is sprayed into the carburettor of a car.

petrol in a bowl

petrol spray

Explain why the spray of petrol burns faster than the petrol in the bowl.

7. Explain each of the following.
    (a) Small sticks of wood burn faster than logs.
    (b) When bellows are used to blow air on to a fire, the fire burns brighter.
    (c) Food is preserved longer when stored in a fridge.
    (d) Plants grow faster in a green-house than in the open-air.
    (e) Large potatoes take longer to cook than small potatoes.
    (f) An oxy-acetylene flame is hot enough to cut through metal.
         The flame obtained by burning acetylene in air is not.

8. The graph shows the volume of carbon dioxide produced in the reaction of
    calcium carbonate powder with dilute hydrochloric acid.

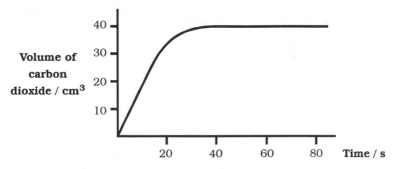

    The experiment was repeated under two different conditions. For both reactions,
    the volume and concentration of the hydrochloric acid remained the same.
    (a) What would have happened to the volume of gas produced in the first 20 s
         when the temperature was increased?
    (b) What would have been the final volume of gas produced when the same
         mass of calcium carbonate lumps was used?

9. Mary was investigating the reaction of marble chips with excess dilute hydrochloric acid. Her results for two experiments are shown below.

(a) What volume of gas was produced in Experiment 1 during the first 90 s?

(b) In the initial stages, the reaction in Experiment 2 was slower than in Experiment 1.

    (i) How can this be concluded from the graph?

    (ii) Suggest **two** changes in conditions which could have resulted in the slower reaction.

(c) Mary used the same mass of marble chips in each experiment. How can this be concluded from the graph?

10. The graph shows the volume of hydrogen produced in the reaction of magnesium ribbon with excess dilute hydrochloric acid.

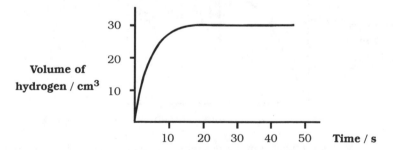

(a) State the volume of hydrogen which was produced after 10 s.

(b) State the time required to produce 20 cm³ of hydrogen.

(c) State the total volume of hydrogen produced.

(d) Copy the graph and add a second curve to show the results that you would expect to obtain if the same mass of magnesium reacted with excess of more concentrated hydrochloric acid.

11. The graph shows the volume of carbon dioxide produced in the reaction of calcium carbonate powder and calcium carbonate lumps with excess dilute hydrochloric acid.

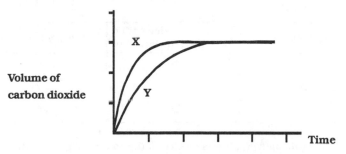

(a) Which curve, **X** or **Y**, shows the results using calcium carbonate powder?

(b) State **three** variables which must be kept the same when comparing the reactions.

12. Pauline was studying rates of reaction. She set up three experiments in which magnesium carbonate was added to equal volumes of dilute hydrochloric acid. In each experiment, some magnesium carbonate remained unreacted.

(a) Place the experiments in order of increasing reaction rate.

(b) Pauline noted the balance readings and found that, at the end of all the experiments, the readings showed a decrease in mass.

Why was the decrease in mass twice as much in Experiment **B** as in Experiment **A**?

13. A company which produces sweets was introducing a new product called "Moon Dust". This sweet was in the form of a powder which fizzed in water. The fizziness was checked before it was put on the market. Three different experiments were carried out.

Experiment	Mass of powder added to 1 litre of water / g	Temperature / °C
1	40	25
2	40	37
3	20	25

For each experiment, a graph was plotted of the volume of gas produced against time.
The graph for Experiment 1 is shown.

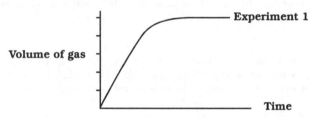

Copy the graph and draw curves to represent Experiment 2 and Experiment 3.

14. George investigated the reaction of magnesium and dilute hydrochloric acid. Here are his notes.

At first the reaction was slow.
The flask got very hot.
The rate of the reaction speeded up.
The reading on the balance fell.
After 5 minutes the reaction had stopped.

(a) Suggest why the reaction speeded up.
(b) Why did the reading on the balance fall during the reaction.

15. Excess zinc powder was added to 100 cm³ of sulphuric acid,concentration 2 mol l⁻¹, at room temperature. The volume of hydrogen produced was plotted against time.

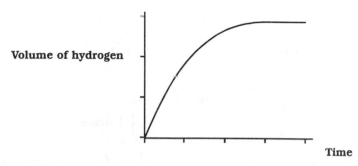

Copy the graph and add the corresponding curves which would be obtained if the reaction is repeated

(a) at a higher temperature,

(b) using zinc granules,

(c) using 100 cm³ of hydrochloric acid, concentration 2 mol l⁻¹,

(d) using 200 cm³ of sulphuric acid, concentration 2 mol l⁻¹.

(Label each curve clearly.)

16. (a) Write balanced equations for the reaction of one mole of each of the following metals with an excess of dilute hydrochloric acid.

    (i) magnesium   (ii) zinc   (iii) sodium

(b) The graph below shows how the volume of hydrogen produced as 0.1 mol of magnesium reacts with excess dilute hydrochloric acid varies with time.

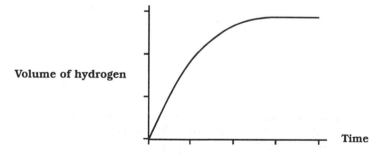

Copy this graph and add corresponding curves for the reactions of

(i) 0.1 mol of zinc (label this curve I),

(ii) 0.1 mol of sodium (label this curve II).

(Assume that the three metals have similar surface areas.)

17. Several experiments were carried out at room temperature with magnesium carbonate and acids. In each case 10 g (excess) of the carbonate was present at the start. The rate of mass loss was studied for various conditions.

Experiment	Acid	MgCO$_3$
A	20 cm^3 HCl(aq), concentration 1 mol l^{-1}	Powdered
B	20 cm^3 HCl(aq), concentration 1 mol l^{-1}	Lump
C	20 cm^3 H$_2$SO$_4$(aq), concentration 1 mol l^{-1}	Powdered
D	10 cm^3 HCl(aq), concentration 1 mol l^{-1}	Powdered

The results of experiment **A** were plotted on a graph.

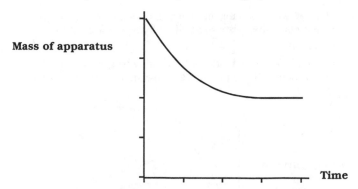

Copy the graph showing reaction **A** and add the corresponding curves which could have been obtained for experiments **B**, **C** and **D**.
(Label each curve clearly.)

18. The collision theory states that for two molecules to react, they must first collide with one another.
    Use the collision theory to explain the effect on reaction rate of
    (a) increasing the concentration of reacting solutions,
    (b) increasing the particle size of a solid.

Intermediate 2 Chemistry

19. Hydrogen peroxide solution decomposes to produce oxygen gas.

$$2H_2O_2(aq) \rightarrow 2H_2O(l) + O_2(g)$$

A pupil carried out the following experiment.

The experiment was repeated with the temperature of the water bath increased by 20 °C.

State how this would affect

(a) the volume of oxygen produced in the first 20 s of the reaction,

(b) the total volume of oxygen produced.

20. The following graph shows the evolution of gas, with time, when two 0.5 g samples of calcium carbonate, each containing insoluble impurities, are reacted with excess dilute hydrochloric acid.

(a) According to the graph, after what time does evolution of gas cease with sample **B**?

(b) State which of the two samples has

(i) the higher purity,

(ii) the smaller particle size.

21. In a "clock reaction" to study reaction rates, iodate ions in acid solution can be reduced to iodine by a solution of sulphite ions. Starch turns blue-black when iodine is formed and can be used as an indicator.

Two experiments were performed at room temperature. In each case, a solution of iodate ions was added to a solution containing sulphite ions and starch. The mixture was stirred and the time measured for the blue-black colour to appear.

Experiment 1

Volume of iodate solution / cm^3	Volume of water / cm^3	Volume of sulphite solution / cm^3	Time / s
25	40	15	13.8
20	45	15	17.0
15	50	15	24.8
10	55	15	35.5
5	60	15	68.7

Experiment 2

Volume of iodate solution / cm^3	Volume of water / cm^3	Volume of sulphite solution / cm^3	Time / s
25	25	30	5.8
20	30	30	8.0
15	35	30	10.0
10	40	30	13.5
5	45	30	24.5

(a) In Experiment 1, which factor affects the reaction rate?

(b) (i) Compared with Experiment 1, which condition is altered in Experiment 2?

   (ii) What effect does this have on the reaction rate?

22. Three experiments were carried out in a study of the rate of reaction between magnesium (in excess) and dilute hydrochloric acid. A balance was used to record the mass of the reaction flask and its contents.
The results of Experiment 1, using magnesium ribbon and 0.4 mol l^{-1} acid are shown in the graph.

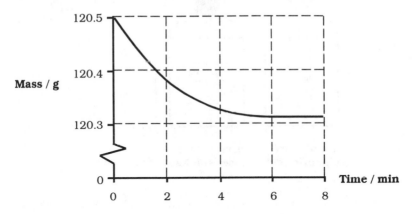

(a) Why did the balance record a decrease in mass during the reaction?

(b) The only difference between Experiment 2 and Experiment 1 was the use of magnesium powder.
Copy the above graph and sketch a curve that could be expected for Experiment 2. (Label it 2.)

(c) The only difference between Experiment 3 and Experiment 1 was the use of 0.2 mol l^{-1} acid.
On the graph, sketch a curve that could be expected for Experiment 3. (Label it 3.)

23. Most polymers are insoluble in water. Some hospitals collect dirty clothing and bedding in bags made from a special polymer which dissolves in hot water. These bags can be sealed and put into washing machines. The risk of infection from touching dirty material is less.

You have been given several samples of different water-soluble polymers and have been asked to find which of them dissolves fastest in warm water.

You are given these instructions.

    1. Pour water into beaker.
    2. Add polymer being tested and start stopclock.
    3. Stir once every 30 s.
    4. When the polymer has completely dissolved, stop the clock.

It is necessary to make fair comparison of the different polymers.

State **two** factors which must be kept the same in all tests.

24. Zinc reacts with sulphuric acid to produce hydrogen.

Adding copper sulphate solution is thought to speed up the reaction.

You are given the chemicals shown in the following diagram:

1 mol / litre   **1 mol / litre**
sulphuric acid **copper sulphate** **zinc lumps**
                          solution

Describe how you would investigate the effect of adding copper sulphate solution on the speed of the reaction between zinc and sulphuric acid.

25. Hydrogen peroxide solution decomposes when heated.

$$2H_2O_2(aq) \rightarrow 2H_2O(l) + O_2(g)$$

The rates of decomposition of 100 cm^3 samples of each solution were followed under three different sets of conditions.

	Concentration of solution / %	Temperature of solution / °C
Curve 1	5.0	80
Curve 2	5.0	90
Curve 3	2.5	80

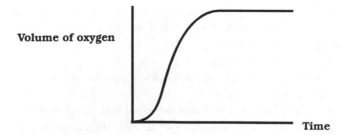

Copy the graph shown for curve 1 and add curves 2 and 3, corresponding to the different conditions.

26. Indigestion can be caused by too much acid in the stomach.Six pupils set up experiments to find out which of two indigestion tablets dissolved in water more quickly. Three used "Calmo" tablets and three used "Easo" tablets.

Calmo
20 °C Andrea   40 °C John   60 °C Kim

Easo
20 °C Naeem   20 °C Kevin   40 °C Kelly

(a) Why would Andrea's and Kevin's experiments, taken together, provide the fairest way of comparing how quickly Calmo and Easo dissolved?

(b) The results of the experiments carried out by Andrea, John and Kim can be compared.

What would this comparison show?

27. A class was asked to measure how the rate at which ice melts is affected by salt. They were provided with the following equipment:

ice cubes in a tray   measuring cylinder   salt

filter funnel   stopclock

Describe the steps which could be used to carry out this investigation using **all the equipment and chemicals listed above**.

Exercise 1.5   Following the course of a reaction

1. In the reaction **R → P**, the concentration of the reactants was measured at
    regular time intervals.

    (a) Draw a rough graph to show how the concentration of reactants (y-axis)
         changes with time. (Label it **R**.)

    (b) Add a curve to show the change in concentration of the products with time.
         (Label it **P**.)

    (c) How do the gradients of the curves relate to the reaction speed?

2. Consider the following graph.

    (a) Calculate the average rate of reaction over the periods
         (i) 0 to 2 minutes,   (ii) 2 to 4 minutes,   (iii) 4 to 6 minutes.

    (b) (i) What happens to the reaction rate as the reaction proceeds?
         (ii) Explain your answer.

3. The reaction between magnesium and dilute hydrochloric acid
         $Mg(s)$ + $2HCl(aq)$ → $MgCl_2(aq)$ + $H_2(g)$
    is followed on a top pan balance.

    (a) Why do the balance readings show a decrease in mass as the reaction
         proceeds?

    (b) Draw a rough graph to show how the balance readings (y-axis) vary
         with time for the reaction.

4. The following graph shows how the volume of the hydrogen produced in a reaction of excess magnesium with dilute acid varies with time.

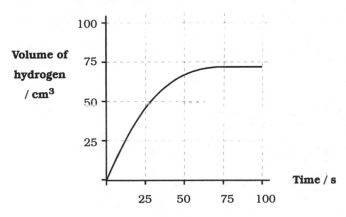

(a) What is the total volume of hydrogen produced in the reaction?
(b) (i) How long does it take for the reaction to go to completion?
     (ii) How long does it take for half of the hydrogen ions in the acid to be reduced to hydrogen?
     (iii) Explain why your answer to ii) is not half your answer to (i).
(c) Calculate the average rate of reaction over the first 25 s.

5. The overall rate of a reaction is often taken as the reciprocal of time (1/time). A graph of rate of reaction against temperature is shown below.

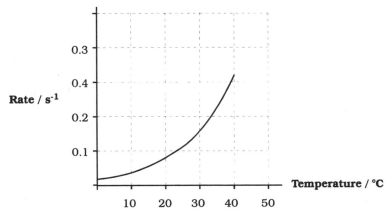

(a) Calculate the time for the reaction when the temperature is 20 °C.
(b) Fu.d the temperature rise required to double the rate of the reaction.
(c) Calculate the rate of the reaction at 50 °C.
(d) Calculate the time taken for the reaction at
     (i)   10°C,   (ii)   20°C,   (iii) 30°C.

6. (a) Draw a rough graph to show how the volume of gas produced (y-axis) varies with time for the reaction:

    $$CaCO_3(s) + 2HCl(aq) \rightarrow CaCl_2(aq) + CO_2(g) + H_2O(l)$$

    (b) For the same reaction, draw a second graph to show how the reaction rate varies with time.

7. Part of a chemistry project involved the study of the reaction between methyl ethanoate and sodium hydroxide solution.

    $$CH_3COOCH_3(aq) + OH^-(aq) \rightarrow CH_3COO^-(aq) + CH_3OH(aq)$$

    The graph below shows the results for one of the experiments.

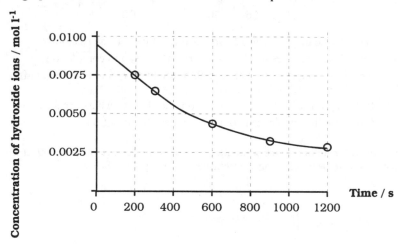

    (a) What was the initial concentration of the sodium hydroxide solution?
    (b) Calculate the average rate of reaction between 200 and 400 s.
    (c) Explain why this was different from the average rate of the reaction during the first 200 s of the reaction.

8. Marble chips, calcium carbonate, reacted with excess dilute hydrochloric acid. The rate of reaction was followed by recording the mass of the container and the reaction mixture over a period of time.
The results of an experiment are shown in the following graph.

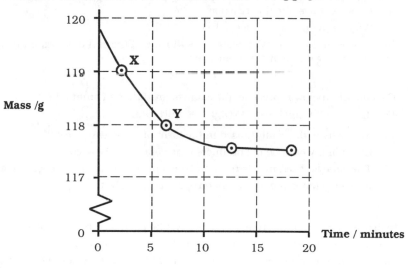

(a) How does the rate of reaction at **X** compare with that at **Y**?

(b) Calculate the average rate of reation over the first 5 minutes.

(c) The half-life of the reaction is the time taken for half of the calcium carbonate to be used up.

Calculate the half-life for this reaction.

(d) Draw a rough graph to show how the volume of gas produced (y-axis) changes over the same period of time.

1.   Hydrogen peroxide solution decomposes to produce oxygen gas. Manganese dioxide is a catalyst for this reaction.

   (a)   What is the purpose of a catalyst?

   (b)   How would the mass of manganese dioxide at the end of an experiment compare with the mass at the start?

2.   The equation below represents the catalytic oxidation of ammonia.

   $$4NH_3(g) \quad + \quad 5O_2(g) \quad \rightarrow \quad 4NO(g) \quad + \quad 6H_2O(g)$$

   (a)   (i)   Why is the catalyst used in the form of a fine wire mesh?

   (ii)   What would be the products if no catalyst were used?

   (b)   The catalyst used in this reaction is an example of a heterogeneous catalyst. Explain what is meant by a **heterogeneous** catalyst.

3.   Hydrogen, for use in the Haber Process, can be produced by the reaction:

   pentane   +   water   →   carbon monoxide   +   hydrogen

   The carbon monoxide formed must be removed or it will poison the catalyst used in the Haber Process.

   (a)   Explain how the catalyst works.

   (b)   Why is the catalyst spread out?

   (c)   What happens when the catalyst is poisoned?

4.   When heated, an aqueous mixture of sodium potassium tartrate and hydrogen peroxide produces oxygen slowly. When a cobalt salt is present in the original mixture, the solution is pink. On warming, oxygen is released rapidly and the colour changes to green. As the effervescence subsides, the colour changes to pink again.

   (a)   Explain these changes in terms of catalysis.

   (b)   What kind of catalyst is involved in the reaction?

5.   The breakdown of fats to form fatty acids in the small intestine is catalysed by a naturally occurring organic substance called lipase.

   (a)   What name is given to organic catalysts such as lipase?

   (b)   Give **one** other naturally-occurring reaction catalysed by an organic catalyst and name the catalyst involved.

6. The graph shows the volume of oxygen produced by the decomposition of hydrogen peroxide under normal conditions.

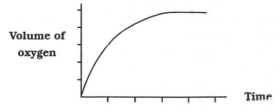

Copy the graph and add a second curve to show the results that you would expect to obtain if the experiment was repeated with the only change being the addition of a catalyst.

7. To reduce the pollutants in exhaust fumes, more and more cars are being fitted with catalytic converters. A typical converter has a honeycomb structure through which the exhaust gases pass. Metal catalysts such as platinum, rhodium and palladium are distributed through the honeycomb.

    (a) Explain why the converter has a honeycomb structure.
    (b) As what kind of catalysts are the metals acting?
    (c) Give **one** reaction which is catalysed by a catalytic converter.
    (d) Explain why "leaded" petrol is not recommended for use with a catalytic converter.

8. Give **one** example of
    (a) a catalyst used in an industrial process and the reaction which it catalyses,
    (b) an enzyme used in an industrial process and the reaction which it catalyses.

9. Reactions take place on the surface of a catalyst. A catalyst can be produced in pellets of different shapes.

Explain which of the shapes **A**, **B**, **C** or **D** would be best for use as a catalyst.

Exercise 1.7   The structure of the atom

1. (a) (i) What name is given to the "core" at the centre of the atom?
        (ii) What charge has this "core"?
    (b) (i) What name is given to the particles which move around the outside of the atom?
        (ii) What charge do these particles have?
    (c) Explain why an atom is neutral.

2. Name the elements with each of the following atomic numbers.
        (a) 23   (b) 3   (c) 18   (d) 28
        (e) 17   (f) 19   (g) 10   (h) 9

3. Copy and complete the following table.

Subatomic particle	Mass	Charge	Location in atom
electron			
proton			
neutron			

4. Name the elements with each of the following electron arrangements.
        (a) 2,8,1   (b) 2,8   (c) 2,8,3
        (d) 2,4   (e) 2,7   (f) 2,8,4

5. Consider this list of elements:

                magnesium, carbon, oxygen, chlorine, sodium, nitrogen

    (a) Which element has an atomic number of 17?
    (b) Which element has 11 electrons in each of its atoms?
    (c) Which element has atoms which have a mass of 12 amu?
    (d) Which element has an electron arrangement of 2,6?

6. (a) Explain what is meant by
        (i) the atomic number,   (ii) the mass number
        of an atom of an element.
    (b) An atom of potassium can be written as $_y^x K$.
        State the information which is given by
        (i) x,
        (ii) y.

7. Calculate the number of protons, neutrons and electrons in each of the following atoms of elements.

(a) $^{23}_{11}Na$ (b) $^{16}_{8}O$ (c) $^{3}_{1}H$

(d) $^{35}_{17}Cl$ (e) $^{1}_{1}H$ (f) $^{40}_{20}Ca$

(g) $^{39}_{19}K$ (h) $^{7}_{3}Li$ (i) $^{32}_{16}S$

8. An atom of sodium can be written as $^{23}_{11}Na$.
   Write each of the atoms below in a similar way.
   (a) An oxygen atom with 10 neutrons.
   (b) An atom, atomic number 6, with 7 neutrons.
   (c) An atom with 17 protons and 20 neutrons.
   (d) An atom of hydrogen, mass number 2.

9. Ernest Rutherford used alpha particles to find out about atomic structures.
   An alpha particle is a positive particle which can gain two electrons to become a neutral atom.
   An alpha particle has a mass number of 4 and an atomic number of 2.
   Calculate the number of protons, neutrons and electrons in an alpha particle.

10. (a) Copy and complete the following table.

Element	Atomic number	Mass number	Number of protons	Number of neutrons	Number of electrons
Ne		22			
N				7	
Ca		40			
A	4	9			
B		14			6
C		89	36		
D			10	10	
E				17	15

(b) Identify elements **A, B, C, D** and **E**.

11. Bromine has a relative atomic mass of 80.
    Analysis of a sample of bromine shows that it contains two isotopes, one with a relative atomic mass of 79 and the other with a relative atomic mass of 81.
    (a) Explain what is meant by isotopes.
    (b) From the information, what can be said about the proportions of the isotopes in the sample?

12. $^{20}_{10}$Ne and $^{22}_{10}$Ne are two different kinds of neon atom.
    (a) In what ways are the kinds of neon atom different?
    (b) Explain why the atoms can be regarded as atoms of the same element.
    (c) What further information is needed to calculate the relative atomic mass of neon?

13. Normal hydrogen atoms, $^{1}_{1}$H, are known as protium atoms.
    (a) (i) How many protons are there in a protium nucleus?
        (ii) How many neutrons are there in a protium nucleus?
        (iii) What name is given to the total number of protons and neutrons in the nucleus of an atom?
    (b) Deuterium, $^{2}_{1}$H, is another type of hydrogen atom.
        (i) How many protons are there in a deuterium nucleus?
        (ii) How many neutrons are there in a deuterium nucleus?
        (iii) Suggest why deuterium is sometimes referred to as "heavy" hydrogen.
    (c) What name is given to pairs of atoms such as protium and deuterium?

14. Two types of lithium atom are $^{6}_{3}$Li and $^{7}_{3}$Li
    Lithium has a relative atomic mass of 6.9.
    (a) What term is used to decribe the different types of lithium atom?
    (b) What can be said about the proportions of each kind of atom in lithium?

15. Atom **A** has mass number 239 and atomic number 93.
    Atom **B** has a mass number 239 and atomic number 94.
    (a) How many protons has **A**?
    (b) How many neutrons has **B**?
    (c) (i) Are atoms **A** and **B** of the same element?
        (ii) Explain your answer.

16. Copper has a relative atomic mass of 63.5. It contains two different kinds of atom: ^{63}Cu and ^{65}Cu
    (a) How many neutrons are present in each kind of atom?
    (b) Which kind of atom is more common in copper?

17. In the reactions occurring in the sun, some atoms collide with such force that their nuclei join together to make one new nucleus.
    (a) Why must a new element be formed in reactions of this kind?
    (b) Helium is formed in solar reactions.
        Nuclei of which element join together to make helium?

Exercise 1.8   The Periodic Table

1. Dimitri Mendeleev used the properties of the elements to help arrange them in his Periodic Table.

   He left gaps in the table if no known element fitted and then made predictions about the properties of the elements that should occupy these gaps.

   (a) Predict whether astatine (atomic number 85) is likely to be a solid, a liquid or a gas at room temperature.

   (b) Predict a chemical property of caesium (atomic number 55).

2. Certain chemicals are added to petrol to prevent "pinking" in car engines.

   Pinking means that the petrol-air mixture explodes too soon.

   It is found that iodine compounds are more effective in preventing pinking than bromine or chlorine compounds.

   Compounds of selenium (atomic number 34) and tellurium (atomic number 52) are both more effective than iodine compounds, with tellurium compounds better than selenium compounds.

   Use this information to explain why the lead compound, tetraethyl lead, is added to some petrols to prevent "pinking".

3. Stephen investigated the formation of solids on mixing solutions.
   He added a few drops of sodium sulphate solution to four other solutions.
   All the solutions had a concentration of 1 mol l^{-1}.

Name of solution	Effect of adding sodium sulphate solution
1. magnesium nitrate	no solid
2. calcium nitrate	slight formation of solid
3. strontium nitrate	solid forms
4. barium nitrate	solid forms

   (a) How would Stephen have been certain that his experiment was fair?

   (b) Predict the effect of adding sodium sulphate to a solution of beryllium nitrate.

4. The reactivity of halogens were
    compared by passing them as
    gases over heated iron wool.

    The results were as follows.

Halogen	Reaction with heated iron wool
Chlorine	The iron wool glows brightly even when the heat is removed.
Bromine	The iron wool gives an orange glow, but only while being heated.
Iodine	The iron wool gives a dull glow, but only while being heated.

    (a) What would you expect to see when fluorine is passed over heated iron
         wool?
    (b) Name the compound formed.

5. Some trends in the reactions of elements and their compounds can be shown on
    the Periodic Table. Here is one example which deals with the extraction of
    metals.

    Key

Source of metal	Extraction method
Soluble compounds	Using electricity
Insoluble compounds	Using electricity
Free metals	———————————
Insoluble oxides / sulphides	Heating with carbon or carbon monoxide

    (a) Using the above information and a Periodic Table in the data booklet,
         suggest an extraction method for strontium (atomic number 38).
    (b) What general statement can be made about the position of a metal in the
         Periodic Table and its ease of extraction?

Intermediate 2 Chemistry

6. The halogens are the elements in Group 7 of the Periodic Table. Their compounds are known as halides.

    Stuart was investigating the reactions between dilute solutions of certain halogens and halides. He added bromine to an iodide and found that iodine was displaced. When he added bromine to a chloride, no reaction took place.

    iodine displaced   **no reaction**

    He carried out more experiments and the results of his investigations are summarised in the following table.

		Halide		
		iodide	bromide	chloride
Halogen	chlorine	√	√	×
	bromine	√	×	×
	iodine	×	×	×

    √ = displacement reaction   × = no reaction

    (a) Use this information to write a general statement about displacement reactions between halogens and halides.

    (b) Predict what would happen if chlorine was added to a fluoride.

7. Refer to the data booklet.

    (a) For each of the compounds shown, decide whether or not 5 g will dissolve in 1 litre of water at room temperature.

        Use one of the following letters for your answer.

        A All the solid will dissolve.

        B Only some of the solid will dissolve.

        C Not enough information is given to decide.

        (i) calcium oxide   (ii) lead(II) iodide   (iii) potassium chloride

    (b) The following compounds are not shown in the data booklet. For each compound predict which letter, vs, s or i, would be used in the table to indicate its solubility.

        (i) rubidium chloride   (ii) radium sulphate

Exercise 1.9   Bonding and structure

1. Explain what is meant by
    (a) a molecule,
    (b) a covalent bond,
    (c) a chemical formula.

2. (a) Explain what is meant by a diatomic molecule.
    (b) Which of the following elements exist as diatomic molecules?
(i) calcium	(ii) carbon	(iii) nitrogen
(iv) aluminium	(v) hydrogen	(vi) neon
(vii) chlorine	(viii) sulphur	(ix) magnesium
(x) oxygen	(xi) fluorine	(xii) argon

3. Draw diagrams to show how the outer electrons form covalent bonds in each of the following molecules.
(a) hydrogen	(b) oxygen
(c) nitrogen	(d) carbon fluoride
(e) hydrogen chloride	(f) hydrogen oxide
(g) phosphorus chloride	(h) carbon dioxide

4.

shared pair of electrons

(a) The atoms in a hydrogen molecule are held together by a covalent bond. A covalent bond is a shared pair of electrons.

Explain how this holds the atoms together.

(b) How does the strength of bonds between different molecules compare with the strength of covalent bonds?

5. (a) Make a drawing to show the shape of each of the following molecules.
    (i) N_2 (ii) CCl_4 (iii) NH_3 (iv) H_2O
    (b) Name the molecule in (a) which is
    (i) linear, (ii) flat.
    (c) What name is given to the shape of a CCl_4 molecule?

6. Study the following list of substances:

sodium chloride, hydrogen chloride, carbon sulphide, aluminium nitrate, iron oxide, phosphorus oxide, copper sulphate, copper, mercury, oxygen, CH_3Cl, MgO, NO_2, Al, $FeCl_2$, Cl_2, C_2H_5OH, Na, Na_2CO_3, $C_6H_{12}O_6$

Arrange the substances in three columns headed covalent bonding, ionic bonding and metallic bonding.

7.

Gas	Relative atomic mass	Density (relative to hydrogen)
hydrogen	1	1
helium	4	2
nitrogen	14	14
oxygen	16	16
neon	20	10
chlorine	35.5	35.5
argon	40	20

(a) Some of the gases in the table are made up of diatomic molecules.

What general statement can be made about the relationship between the relative atomic mass and density (relative to hydrogen) for the diatomic molecules?

(b) If the relative atomic mass of xenon is 131, predict its density (relative to hydrogen).

8. The covalent bonds in water are highly polar.

(a) Why are polar covalent bonds formed in water?

(b) Name **three** substances with covalent bonds which are **not** polar.

9. Carbon dioxide is made up of discrete molecules but silicon dioxide has a covalent network structure.

Explain what is meant by

(a) discrete molecules

(b) a covalent network structure.

10. With the aid of a diagram, describe the type of bonding and structure found in copper metal.

11. (a) Explain clearly what happens when

(i) an atom of chlorine forms a chloride ion,

(ii) an atom of calcium forms a calcium ion.

(b) What happens during the formation of an ionic bond in calcium chloride?

12. (a) Copy and complete the following table to show the numbers of protons and electrons in each of the following ions.

Ion	Number of protons	Number of electrons
Ca^{2+}		
Cl^-		
Al^{3+}		
O^{2-}		

(b) Look at the information in the table.

Ion	Number of protons	Number of electrons
zinc	30	28
sulphide	16	18
copper	29	28
tin	50	48

Using the information in the table, show how you would represent

  (i) the zinc ion,   (ii) the copper ion,

  (iii) the sulphide ion,   (iv) the tin ion.

13. A compound is formed from a Group 1 element and a Group 7 element.

Choose two elements and show by means of a diagram what happens to the electrons in the outer energy level (shell) of the atoms involved.

14. Hydrogen chloride is made up of molecules but sodium chloride exists as a lattice.

(a) Explain what is meant by a lattice.

(b) Explain why the word "molecule" has no meaning when we are thinking of sodium chloride.

15. The chemical formulae for three substances and their types of structures are shown in the table.

Name of compound	Chemical formula	Type of structure
sulphur trioxide	SO_3	discrete molecular
magnesium chloride	$MgCl_2$	ionic
silicon oxide	SiO_2	covalent network

State the different information given by each chemical formula.

Exercise 1.10   Properties

1.   (a) By means of a labelled diagram, show the experimental apparatus which can be used to classify substances into conductors and non-conductors.

     (b) Study the following list of solids:

> nickel, iodine, copper, magnesium, sulphur, phosphorus, sodium, scandium

     Arrange the solids in two columns, headed conductors and non-conductors.

     (c) Study the following list of liquids:

> petrol, copper sulphate solution, silicon tetrachloride, hexene, liquid oxygen, molten sulphur, sodium chloride solution, mercury, strontium nitrate solution, molten iron

     Arrange the liquids in two columns, headed conductors and non-conductors.

2.   Study the following list of substances:

> glucose, sulphur, sodium bromide, paraffin wax, silicon dioxide, silver, carbon tetrachloride, potassium, nickel chloride

     (a) Name the substances which conduct electricity when solid.

     (b) (i) Name the substances which conduct electricity when in aqueous solution.

          (ii) Explain why the substances you have chosen do **not** conduct when solid.

3.   The electrical conductivities of substances **A**, **B** and **C** were measured and the results are shown.

Substance	In solid state	Dissolved in water	In molten state
A	0	+	+
B	+	insoluble	+
C	0	0	0

        + conducts well   0 non-conductor

     (a) Which substance could be lead?

     (b) Which substance could be potassium bromide?

     (c) Which substance could be iodine?

4.

	P	Q	R	S
Solubility in water	soluble	insoluble	soluble	soluble
Colour of solution	colourless	-	blue	colourless
Electrical conductivity in solid state	does not conduct	conducts	does not conduct	does not conduct
Electrical conductivity in molten state	does not conduct	conducts	conducts	conducts

Some properties of four substances

         sodium chloride,   copper bromide,   aluminium,   glucose

are given in the table above.

(a) Use the table to identify the four substances **P**, **Q**, **R**, and **S**.

(b) State the type of chemical bonding in substances **P**, **R**, and **S**.

(c) Explain why

    (i) substance **Q** conducts electricity in the solid state,

    (ii) substances **R** and **S** do not conduct when solid but do conduct in the molten state.

5. (a) Draw a labelled diagram to show an experiment you would carry out to test whether a substance is ionic or covalent.

(b) The table below shows some properties of two chlorides.

Chloride	mp /°C	bp /°C	Solubility in water
XCl	801	1417	soluble
YCl$_4$	-23	77	insoluble

    (i) Which of these chlorides would you expect to be covalent and which is likely to be ionic?

    (ii) In which group of the Periodic Table would you expect to find element **X**?

6. The compounds **P, Q, R** and **S** all contain chlorine.

Chloride	P	Q	R	S
Boiling point / °C	1690	62	76	1412
Melting point / °C	1074	-63	-112	708

(a) Which of these chlorides are liquid at room temperature?
(Assume room temperature to be 25 °C .)

(b) State which of these have a discrete molecular structure.

7. A pupil investigated the properties of three compounds. The results are shown in the table.

Substance	Melting point	Electrical conduction
A	high	does not conduct in any state
B	low	does not conduct in any state
C	high	conducts in solution and as melt

Explain whether the structure in **A, B** and **C** is discrete covalent, covalent network or ionic.

8. Explain each of the following.
(a) Sodium oxide is a solid at room temperature.
(b) Carbon dioxide is a gas at room temperature.
(c) Silicon oxide is a solid at room temperature.

9. The average composition of a bottle of drinking water is shown.

Cations	Mass /mg	Anions	Mass /mg
calcium	1	hydrogencarbonate	5
magnesium	1	chloride	25
potassium	3	sulphate	5
sodium	16	nitrate	0

(a) Which cation will give a yellow colour in a flame test?
(You may wish to refer to the data booklet to help you.)

(b) What do all these anions have in common.

(c) Suggest a reason for samples of drinking water from various parts of the country having different conductivities.

10. Titanium is used in the making of supersonic aircraft and space vehicles.

To extract titanium, rutile, a titanium ore, is first converted into titanium(IV) chloride. This is then reduced to the metal by heating it with sodium or magnesium in an atmosphere of argon.

(a) Suggest why it is necessary to carry out the reduction of titanium(IV) chloride in an atmosphere of argon.

(b) Titanium(IV) chloride is a liquid at room temperature.

What does this indicate about the type of bonding in titanium(IV) chloride.

11. The following table shows the properties of four substances.

Property	P	Q	R	S
appearance	sparkling solid	silvery liquid	white solid	colourless liquid
solubilty in water	insoluble	insoluble	soluble	soluble
electrical conductivity	does not conduct	conducts when solid or molten	conducts when molten or in solution	does not conduct
melting point /°C	3547	-61	801	-115
boiling point /°C	4827	357	1417	59

For each of **P**, **Q**, **R** and **S**, explain whether the substance is likely to be a metal, an ionic compound or a covalent compound (discrete molecular or network).

Exercise 1.11   Electrolysis

1. A pupil carried out experiments to investigate what happens during the electrolysis of melts.

   (a) Explain what is meant by electrolysis.

   (b) Name the products at the positive and negative electrode in the electrolysis of melts of each of the following compounds.

      (i) magnesium chloride   (ii) sodium iodide

      (iii) lead bromide   (iv) calcium oxide

2. Several groups of pupils carried out the same experiment using the apparatus shown. One group found the results shown in Table 1, while all the other groups found the results shown in Table 2.

Time	Table 1	Table 2
before heating	bulb not lit	bulb not lit
during heating	bulb lights	bulb lights
when apparatus has cooled	bulb stays lit	bulb goes out

   (a) Explain why most groups obtained the results in Table 2.

   (b) Name the product formed at each electrode.

   (c) Give a possible reason for the faulty results at the end of the experiment in Table 1.

3. Paul connected a low voltage supply to carbon electrodes in a copper chloride solution. He wrote some notes in his jotter.

   > Observations
   > A gas was given off at the positive electrode.
   > The other carbon rod turned brown.

   (a) What type of experiment did Paul carry out?

   (b) Name the gas given off at the positive electrode.

   (c) Explain why the negative electrode "turned brown".

4.

With a battery as a power supply, hydrochloric acid can be electrolysed using carbon electrodes. During the electrolysis, chlorine gas is given off at the positive electrode and hydrogen gas is given off at the negative electrode.

(a) Copy and label the above diagram.

(b) Why is chlorine gas given off at the positive electrode?

(c) Suggest a reason why the electrodes are **not** made of iron.

5. Electricity is used to obtain aluminium from a molten mixture containing bauxite (aluminium oxide).

(a) Why does the mixture need to be kept molten?

(b) Explain why aluminium is formed at the negative electrode.

6. A pupil carried out an experiment to investigate the products of the electrolysis of nickel bromide solution.

(a) Explain why a d.c. supply is used for this experiment.

(b) Explain what would be seen at the negative electrode.

(c) Explain what would be seen at the positive electrode.

(d) Explain why carbon tetrabromide solution **cannot** be changed in the same way.

7. Water in swimming pools can be purified using a chlorinating cell. Sodium
    chloride solution is electrolysed in the cell to produce chlorine.

sodium chloride powder

water from pool   pump   chlorinating cell   chlorinated water to pool

(a) Why can solid sodium chloride **not** be electrolysed?

(b) (i)   At which electrode is chlorine produced?

     (ii) Describe what is happening in the formation of chlorine.

8. Mr Young gave his class three bottles labelled **A**, **B** and **C**.

    They contained silver nitrate solution, dilute hydrochloric acid and glucose
    solution.

    He asked the class to use the following apparatus to identify the solutions.

low voltage d.c. supply

ammeter

carbon electrodes

solution

Here are the results for one group of pupils.

Solution	Meter reading	Observations at electrodes
A	no	no reaction
B	yes	grey solid at negative electrode
C	yes	a gas formed at both electrodes

(a) (i)   Identify solution **A**.

     (ii) What type of bonding must **A** have?

(b) Identify solution **B**.

(c) Name the gas formed at the positive electrode when solution **C** is used.

9. Shown below is a list of compounds and their colours.

sodium chloride	white	sodium sulphate	white
sodium selenate	white	copper sulphate	blue
nickel sulphate	green	vanadium sulphate	violet

State the colour of

(a) copper selenate,   (b) vanadium chloride,   (c) nickel chloride.

10. A crystal of copper dichromate was placed on moist filter paper at position **X**. When a high voltage was applied, a blue colour moved towards the negative electrode while an orange colour moved towards the positive electrode.

(a) (i) What can be learned from this experiment about the colour and charge of the dichromate ion?

     (ii) Explain your answer.

(b) State any safety precaution which should be observed in this experiment.

11.

(a) (i) What will happen when the current is switched on?

     (ii) Explain your answer.

(b) What will happen if the current is reversed?

12.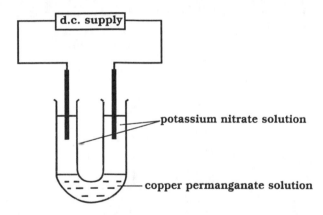

potassium nitrate solution

copper permanganate solution

The apparatus shown is used to demonstrate the electrolysis of copper permanganate solution.

(a) Why is potassium nitrate solution used instead of water?

(b) Potassium chloride is white while potassium permanganate is purple. What is the colour of the permanganate ion?

(c) (i) What will be observed after passing the current in the above apparatus for about 20 minutes?

(ii) Explain your answer.

13. An electric current was passed through different solutions. The results are shown in the table.

Solution	Positive electrode product	Negative electrode product
hydrochloric acid	chlorine	hydrogen
potassium chloride	chlorine	hydrogen
sulphuric acid	oxygen	hydrogen
sodium nitrate	oxygen	hydrogen
nitric acid	oxygen	hydrogen
silver nitrate	oxygen	silver

(a) From the results, suggest a general statement which can be made about acids.

(b) From the results, predict the products at the positive and negative electrodes, if potassium nitrate is used.

(c) Explain why potassium chloride conducts electricity when dissolved in water but **not** when solid.

14. Gillian investigated the ability of different substances to conduct electricity when dissolved in water.

Here are her results.

Substance	Concentration of solution in mol l^{-1}	Current in mA
sodium chloride	0.005	21
sodium chloride	0.002	11
sodium chloride	0.001	7
hydrochloric acid	0.005	62
hydrochloric acid	0.002	27
hydrochloric acid	0.001	20
sodium hydroxide	0.005	32
sodium hydroxide	0.002	15
sodium hydroxide	0.001	11

(a) What name is used to describe a solution which conducts electricity?

(b) Identify **two** variables which she would have kept constant to make sure that her results were fair.

(c) From the results, state the effect of changing concentration on the ability of a substance to conduct electricity when dissolved in water.

(d) Arrange the three substances in order of their ability to conduct electricity when dissolved in water. (Put the best conductor first.)

Exercise 1.12   Formulae (i)

1. Write the chemical formula for each of the following substances.

(a)

(b)   H — H

(c)

(d)

(e)

2. The molecules below show the way atoms are arranged in different molecules. Choose a name for each substance from the following list:

   chlorine,   hydrogen oxide,   carbon chloride,   nitrogen,
   hydrogen chloride,   nitrogen hydride,   oxygen

(a)

(b)

(c)

(d)

(e)

(f)

(g)

3. Write the chemical formula for each of the following compounds.

(a) sulphur trioxide   (b) carbon dioxide
(c) carbon monoxide   (d) silicon tetrafluoride
(e) phosphorus pentachloride (f) uranium hexafluoride

Exercise 1.13   Formulae (ii)

1. Write the chemical formula for each of the following covalent compounds.
    (a) hydrogen oxide   (b) phosphorus fluoride
    (c) nitrogen chloride   (d) hydrogen iodide
    (e) sulphur chloride   (f) silicon oxide

2. Write the chemical formula for each of the following ionic compounds
    compounds.
    (a) sodium bromide   (b) potassium chloride
    (c) magnesium chloride   (d) calcium sulphide
    (e) aluminium oxide   (f) magnesium oxide
    (g) lithium hydroxide   (h) potassium sulphate
    (i) caesium nitrate   (j) potassium carbonate
    (k) strontium sulphate   (l) ammonium chloride

3. Write the chemical formula for each of the following ionic compounds.
    (a) calcium hydroxide   (b) barium nitrate
    (c) magnesium nitrite   (d) ammonium sulphate
    (e) calcium nitrate   (f) aluminium hydroxide

4. Write the chemical formula for each of the following ionic compounds.
    (a) lead(II) bromide   (b) copper(I) oxide
    (c) iron(II) chloride   (d) nickel(II) sulphate
    (e) iron(II) carbonate   (f) copper(II) hydroxide
    (g) silver(I) nitrate   (h) vanadium(V) oxide

5. Write the symbol or chemical formula for each of the following substances.
    (a) sodium chloride   (b) carbon monoxide
    (c) magnesium hydroxide   (d) hydrogen chloride
    (e) oxygen   (f) iron(III) chloride
    (g) potassium hydroxide   (h) sodium
    (i) ammonium bromide   (j) hydrogen
    (k) rubidium fluoride   (l) sulphur chloride
    (m) magnesium sulphate   (n) ammonium carbonate
    (o) iron   (p) copper(II) oxide
    (q) sodium sulphide   (r) hydrogen fluoride

6. Alums are a group of ionic compounds. Some of them are shown in the table.

Common name	Chemical name	Formula
ammonium alum	aluminium ammonium sulphate	$NH_4Al(SO_4)_2$
chrome alum	chromium(III) potassium sulphate	$KCr(SO_4)_2$
potash alum	A	$KAl(SO_4)_2$
ferric alum	ammonium iron(III) sulphate	B

(a) Write the chemical name for potash alum, **A**.

(b) Write the chemical formula for ferric alum, **B**.

Exercise 1.14

Equations (i)

1. In a chemical reaction, atoms of elements are rearranged. The atoms that are the in the products are from the same elements as those in the reactants.

   (a) Which of the following gases may be obtained by heating copper(II) carbonate ($CuCO_3$)?

      (i) oxygen   (ii) hydrogen
      (iii) carbon dioxide   (iv) nitrogen

   (b) Which of the following gases may **not** be obtained by heating sodium chromate (Na_2CrO_4)?

      (i) oxygen   (ii) hydrogen
      (iii) carbon dioxide   (iv) nitrogen

   (c) Which of the following gases may be obtained when calcium reacts with water?

      (i) oxygen   (ii) hydrogen
      (iii) carbon dioxide   (iv) nitrogen

   (d) Which of the following gases may **not** be obtained when dilute hydrochloric acid (HCl) reacts with calcium sulphate ($CaSO_4$)?

      (i) oxygen   (ii) hydrogen
      (iii) chlorine   (iv) sulphur dioxide
      (v) carbon dioxide   (vi) nitrogen

2. Write word equations for each of the following chemical reactions.

   (a) When magnesium metal burns, it reacts with oxygen of the air to form magnesium oxide, a white powder.

   (b) In the Blast furnace, iron is made by reacting iron ore with carbon monoxide gas. Carbon dioxide gas is also produced.

   (c) In our bodies, starch which we get from our food, breaks down to form glucose, which can pass through the walls of our intestines, and water.

   (d) When calcium metal is added to water, a gas is given off and calcium hydroxide solution is formed. When tested with a burning splint, the gas burns with a "pop".

   (e) Copper oxide powder and a gas which turns limewater milky are made when copper carbonate powder is heated.

3. Write a sentence to describe the following reactions. The first one is done for you.

(a) $C(s) + O_2(g) \rightarrow CO_2(g)$

Carbon solid is reacting with oxygen gas to form carbon dioxide gas.

(b) $CO(g) + O_2(g) \rightarrow CO_2(g)$

(c) $C(s) + Cl_2(g) \rightarrow CCl_4(l)$

(d) $H_2(g) + F_2(g) \rightarrow HF(g)$

(e) $SO_2(g) + O_2(g) \rightarrow SO_3(g)$

(f) $CuO(s) + CO(g) \rightarrow Cu(s) + CO_2(g)$

(g) $NH_3(g) \rightarrow N_2(g) + H_2(g)$

(h) $CH_4(g) + O_2(g) \rightarrow CO_2(g) + H_2O(l)$

(i) $HBr(g) \rightarrow H_2(g) + Br_2(l)$

Exercise 1.15

Equations (ii)

In the questions in this exercise it is not necessary to balance the equations.

1. Use symbols and formulae to write chemical equations for each of the following reactions.
   (a) carbon + oxygen → carbon monoxide
   (b) sulphur + oxygen → sulphur dioxide
   (c) hydrogen chloride → hydrogen + chlorine
   (d) nitrogen + oxygen → nitrogen dioxide
   (e) phosphorus + chlorine → phosphorus chloride

2. Use symbols and formulae to write chemical equations for each of the following reactions.
   (a) calcium + oxygen → calcium oxide
   (b) sodium + chlorine → sodium chloride
   (c) magnesium + sulphuric acid, H_2SO_4(aq)
         → magnesium sulphate + hydrogen
   (d) magnesium + carbon dioxide → magnesiun oxide + carbon
   (e) barium chloride solution + sodium sulphate solution
         → sodium chloride solution + barium sulphate solid
   (f) calcium carbonate + hydrochloric acid, HCl(aq)
         → calcium chloride + carbon dioxide + water

3. Use symbols and formulae to write chemical equations for each of the following reactions.
   (a) the burning of hydrogen
   (b) the reaction of sodium with water to form sodium hydroxide and hydrogen
   (c) the reaction of silicon with chlorine
   (d) the decomposition of silver(I) oxide
   (e) the burning of ethene (C_2H_4) to form carbon dioxide and water
   (f) the formation of hydrogen iodide
   (g) the burning of magnesium
   (h) the decomposition of nitrogen hydride
   (i) the decomposition of copper(II) carbonate to form copper(II) oxide and carbon dioxide

52

Intermediate 2 Chemistry

1. Balance each of the following equations.

   (a) $C + O_2 \rightarrow CO_2$

   (b) $P + Cl_2 \rightarrow PCl_3$

   (c) $C + Br_2 \rightarrow CBr_4$

   (d) $C_4H_8 + O_2 \rightarrow CO_2 + H_2O$

   (e) $H_2O_2 \rightarrow H_2O + O_2$

2. Write balanced chemical equations for each of the following reactions.

   (a) carbon monoxide + oxygen $\rightarrow$ carbon dioxide

   (b) hydrogen + chlorine $\rightarrow$ hydrogen chloride

   (c) methane (CH_4) + oxygen $\rightarrow$ carbon dioxide + water

   (d) sulphur dioxide + oxygen $\rightarrow$ sulphur trioxide

   (e) phosphorus + chlorine $\rightarrow$ phosphorus chloride

3. Balance each of the following equations.

   (a) $Mg(s) + O_2(g) \rightarrow MgO(s)$

   (b) $Mg(s) + AgNO_3(aq) \rightarrow Mg(NO_3)_2(aq) + Ag(s)$

   (c) $NaOH(aq) + H_2SO_4(aq) \rightarrow Na_2SO_4(aq) + H_2O(l)$

   (d) $AgNO_3(aq) + BaCl_2(aq) \rightarrow Ba(NO_3)_2(aq) + AgCl(s)$

   (e) $Na(s) + H_2O(l) \rightarrow NaOH(aq) + H_2(g)$

   (f) $Al(s) + Cl_2(g) \rightarrow AlCl_3(s)$

4. Write balanced chemical equations for each of the following reactions.

   (a) sodium + oxygen $\rightarrow$ sodium oxide

   (b) magnesium + sulphur dioxide $\rightarrow$ magnesium oxide + sulphur

   (c) calcium + water $\rightarrow$ calcium hydroxide + hydrogen

   (d) calcium oxide + sulphuric acid, $H_2SO_4(aq)$

   $\rightarrow$ calcium sulphate + water

   (e) potassium carbonate + hydrochloric acid, HCl(aq)

   $\rightarrow$ potassium chloride + water + carbon dioxide

   (f) potassium sulphate solution + barium nitrate solution

   $\rightarrow$ potassium nitrate solution + barium sulphate solid

5. Write balanced chemical equations for each of the following reactions.
   (a) the formation of sulphur trioxide from sulphur dioxide and oxygen
   (b) the reaction of magnesium with fluorine
   (c) the combination of carbon with chlorine
   (d) the burning of camping GAZ (C_3H_8) to form carbon dioxide and water
   (e) the burning of aluminium
   (f) the reaction of nitrogen hydride with oxygen to form nitrogen and water
   (g) the combustion of acetylene (C_2H_2) to form carbon dioxide and water
   (h) the reaction of hydrogen and copper(II) oxide to form copper and water

6. Write balanced chemical equations for each of the following reactions.
   (a) sodium hydroxide solution and sulphuric acid
   (b) magnesium oxide and nitric acid
   (c) potassium carbonate solution and hydrochloric acid
   (d) aluminium and sulphuric acid

7. Write balanced chemical equations for each of the following reactions.
   (a) silver(I) nitrate solution and sodium chloride solution
   (b) sodium hydroxide solution and lead(II) chloride solution
   (c) barium chloride solution and sodium sulphate solution
   (d) calcium nitrate solution and potassium carbonate solution
   (e) iron(III) chloride solution and barium hydroxide solution

8. "Superpure" germanium is used in transistors. There are three steps in the process used to purify the germanium.

Step 1.	Germanium combines directly with chlorine.
Step 2.	Water is added to the germanium oxide to form germanium dioxide and hydrogen chloride.
Step 3.	Germanium dioxide reacts with hydrogen to form germanium and water.

   Write balanced chemical equations for each reaction in Steps 1, 2 and 3.

9. Some elements exist as diatomic molecules.
   Two such elements, formulae X_2 and Y_2, react together to form a compound.
   An experiment shows that 1 mole of element **X** reacts exactly with 2 moles of element **Y** to give 2 moles of compound.
   Use this information to derive the formula for the compound formed between **X** and **Y**.

Exercise 1.17   The mole

1. Calculate the formula mass of each of the following substances.
    - (a) H_2O
    - (b) CH_4
    - (c) $CaCO_3$
    - (d) Na_2SO_4
    - (e) $Mg(NO_3)_2$
    - (f) nitrogen hydride
    - (g) carbon dioxide
    - (h) potassium carbonate
    - (i) aluminium oxide
    - (j) ammonium chloride

2. Calculate the mass of one mole of each of the following substances.
    - (a) C_3H_6
    - (b) MgO
    - (c) K_2CO_3
    - (d) $C_6H_{12}O_6$
    - (e) $(NH_4)_2SO_4$
    - (f) magnesium chloride
    - (g) calcium oxide
    - (h) potassium hydroxide
    - (i) magnesium sulphate
    - (j) sodium nitrate

3. Calculate the mass of each of the following substances.
    - (a) 2 mol of sodium
    - (b) 0.1 mol of $CaSO_4$
    - (c) 0.25 mol of $MgNO_3$
    - (d) 5 mol of sulphur dioxide
    - (e) 0.2 mol of magnesium oxide
    - (f) 0.5 mol of ammonium carbonate

4. Calculate the number of moles in each of the following substances.
    - (a) 36 g of carbon
    - (b) 5.6 g of CO
    - (c) 4 g of NaOH
    - (d) 2.06 g of lithium sulphate
    - (e) 8.2 g of calcium nitrate
    - (f) 2.9 kg of magnesium hydroxide

5. The composition of 9-carat gold is shown in the pie chart.
    A 9-carat gold ring weighs 7.88 g
    Calculate the number of moles of gold in the ring.

6. Heavy water is made up of molecules in which each of the hydrogen atoms has one neutron in its nucleus.
    Calculate the number of moles of heavy water molecules in 500 g of heavy water.

7. The filling for a tooth is often made of dental amalgam. The pie chart shows the composition of a typical dental amalgam.

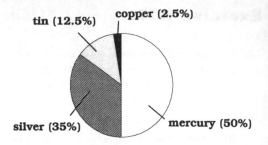

Calculate the number of moles of mercury in 2.0 g of dental amalgam.

8. The following table shows the formula mass of various gases.

Gas	ammonia	argon	carbon monoxide	ethane	oxygen
Formula mass	17	40	28	20	32

(a) Use your data booklet to find the density of the five gases and draw a **line graph** of density against formula mass.

(b) A compound of carbon, hydrogen and fluorine has a density of 1.51 kg / m^{-3}.

    (i) Use your line graph to find the formula mass of the gas.

    (ii) Give the formula for this gas.

9. Toners for colouring black and white photographs are made by mixing two solutions. The solutions should be made up using warm water.

Solution 1	Solution 2
Sodium sulphide solution concentration 100 g / l	Sodium hydroxide solution concentration 80 g / l

(a) Calculate the concentration of the sodium hydroxide solution in mol l^{-1}.

(b) Different colours are obtained by mixing the two solutions.

| Colour | Toner composition | |
	Volume of sodium sulphide solution / cm^3	Volume of sodium hydroxide solution / cm^3
cold brown	10	40
brown	20	30
warm brown	30	20

What mass of sodium sulphide will be required to make 100 cm^3 of toner for a cold brown colour?

Exercise 1.18   Using balanced equations

1. $Mg(s)$ + $Cl_2(g)$ → $MgCl_2(s)$
Calculate the mass of magnesium chloride produced in the reaction of 1.2 g of magnesium with excess chlorine.

2. $CH_4(g)$ + $2O_2(g)$ → $CO_2(g)$ + $2H_2O(g)$
Calculate the mass of carbon dioxide produced in the reaction of 3.2 g of methane (CH_4) with excess oxygen.

3. $4Na(s)$ + $O_2(g)$ → $2Na_2O(s)$
Calculate the mass of sodium oxide produced in the reaction of 2.3 g of sodium with excess oxygen.

4. $N_2(g)$ + $3H_2(g)$ → $2NH_3(g)$
Calculate the mass of hydrogen required to react with 56 g of nitrogen.

5. $4Al(s)$ + $3O_2(g)$ → $2Al_2O_3(s)$
Calculate the mass of oxygen required to react with 2.7 g of aluminium.

6. $Mg(s)$ + $CuSO_4(aq)$ → $MgSO_4(aq)$ + $Cu(s)$
Calculate the mass of copper produced in the reaction of 1.2 g of magnesium with excess copper(II) sulphate.

7.   As a result of recycling, an industrial plant converts 7.7×10^4 kg of hydrogen to ammonia each day.
        $N_2(g)$ + $3H_2(g)$ → $2NH_3(g)$
Calculate the mass of ammonia which is produced each day.

8.   Ammonium sulphate is a fertiliser. The compound can be produced by the reaction of ammonia with sulphuric acid.
        $2NH_3(g)$ + $H_2SO_4(aq)$ → $(NH_4)_2SO_4$
Calculate the mass of ammonium sulphate which could be produced from 170 kg of ammonia.

9.   Ammonia can be formed by adding water to magnesium nitride.
        $Mg_3N_2(s) + 6H_2O (l)$ → $3Mg(OH)_2(s) + 2NH_3(g)$
Calculate the mass of ammonia produced when 30 g of magnesium nitride are added to excess water.

10. A power station produces sulphur dioxide, an atmospheric pollutant.

    The sulphur dioxide can be removed by reaction with limestone (calcium carbonate).

    $$CaCO_3 \;+\; SO_2 \;\rightarrow\; CaSO_3 \;+\; CO_2$$

    Calculate the mass of calcium carbonate required to remove completely 580 tonnes of sulphur dioxide.

11. The monomer for polythene can be produced from ethanol.

| ethanol | ethene | water |

    Calculate the maximum mass of ethene which can be produced from 6900 kg of ethanol.

12. Nitrogen is used to fill the air-bags which protect people in car crashes.

    It is produced when sodium azide (NaN_3) decomposes rapidly.

    $$2NaN_3(s) \;\rightarrow\; 2Na(s) \;+\; 3N_2(g)$$

    A driver's air-bag contains 60 g of sodium azide.

    Calculate the mass of nitrogen gas which would be produced.

13. Octane burns in a plentiful supply of air to produce carbon dioxide and water.

    $$C_8H_{18}(l) \;+\; 12\tfrac{1}{2}O_2(g) \;\rightarrow\; 8CO_2(g) \;+\; 9H_2O(g)$$

    Calculate the mass of carbon dioxide produced by the burning of 57 tonnes of octane.

Unit 2

Exercise 2.1   Fuels

1. Petrol is an important <u>fuel</u>. The <u>combustion</u> of petrol is an important reaction. Explain what is meant by each of the terms underlined.

2. You are given three unlabelled cylinders of gas.
Each cylinder contains one of the following gases.

oxygen,   nitrogen,   carbon dioxide

Describe how to find out which gas is contained in each cylinder.

3. Crude oil is a mixture of chemical compounds. Before the compounds can be used, the crude oil must be separated into fractions, by fractional distillation.

    (a) Name the kind of chemical compounds found in crude oil.

    (b) Explain what is meant by

      (i) fractional distillation,

      (ii) a fraction.

    crude oil →

    (c) Give a use for each of the following products obtained from oil.

      (i) petrol   (ii) diesel   (iii) gas

      (iv) kerosine   (v) bitumen

4. (a) Explain what is meant by

      (i) a flammable substance,

      (ii) a viscous substance.

    (b) Consider the following substances obtained from oil:

    petrol,   diesel,   gas,   kerosine,   bitumen

    Name the fraction which is

      (i) most flammable,

      (ii) most viscous.

5. (a) Name the **two** gases which are the main components of air.

    (b) Explain why these gases can combine inside a car engine.

6. Powdered limestone (calcium carbonate) is used to remove sulphur dioxide from the gases given off in a coal-fired power station.
Limestone is insoluble in water. A soluble carbonate would be more efficient.

    (a) Why should sulphur dioxide be removed?

    (b) Suggest why limestone is used rather than a soluble carbonate.

7. In a paraffin burner, heat is produced when the paraffin burns.
   (a) What term is used to describe a reaction which produces heat?
   (b) Which gas is used up when paraffin burns?
   (c) What are the **two** products when paraffin burns in plenty of air?
   (d) Explain why it is dangerous to burn paraffin in a very poorly ventilated room.

8. The burning of petrol can cause pollution of the air.
   (a) Why does burning petrol in a car engine produce carbon monoxide as well as carbon dioxide?
   (b) Name the poisonous gas which can be formed from sulphur compounds when petrol is burned.
   (c) Explain why air pollution is more of a problem in industrial areas.
   (d) State **one** way of reducing air pollution from the burning of the hydrocarbons in petrol.

9. British motorists throw away about 30 million old rubber tyres every year. Two ways of recycling old tyres are being tried.
   (1) Burn them in power stations where sulphur dioxide formed can be taken out.
   (2) Break up the long chain molecules by heating the tyres to a high temperature in the absence of air. This produces a mixture of hydrocarbon molecules.
   (a) Name **three** elements present in the rubber.
   (b) Name the process which could be used to separate the hydrocarbon molecules in the mixture into useful groups.

10. Fires in coal mines can be caused by coal dust.
    (a) Which element in air is needed for the coal dust to burn?
    (b) Why is coal dust likely to cause explosions?
    (c) In a limited supply of air, coal fires can produce a poisonous gas. Name this gas.

11. Coal is a source of other chemicals.

   (a) Coal gas is a mixture of hydrogen and carbon monoxide. These gases can be combined to form methanal

   hydrogen + carbon monoxide → methanal

   Name **all** the elements present in methanal.
   (b) Coal tar contains hydrocarbons.
   Explain what is meant by a hydrocarbon.

12. Crude oil contains a mixture of chemicals. The table compares the composition of a sample of crude oil from the North Sea with one from an oil field in the Middle East.

Chemicals	% of chemicals in two samples of oil	
	North Sea crude	Middle East crude
gases and gasoline	7	6
petroleum spirit	20	14
kerosene and diesel	30	25
residue chemicals	43	55

(a) Use the information in the table to suggest **one** reason why North Sea crude oil might be more useful than Middle East crude oil for modern day needs.

(b) Name the process used to separate the different chemicals in crude oil.

13. Consider the following substances obtained from fractions of crude oil:

   petrol, diesel, kerosine, gas, bitumen

(a) Name the substance which contains molecules with carbon atoms in the following ranges.

 (i) C1 to C4   (ii) C4 to C12   (iii) C9 to C16

 (iv) C15 to C25   (v) more than C70

(b) (i) Which has the higher boiling point, petrol or bitumen?

 (ii) Explain your answer.

14. Sulphur dioxide is one of the causes of acid rain. The bar graph shows the amount of sulphur dioxide released during four years from burning coal in the UK.

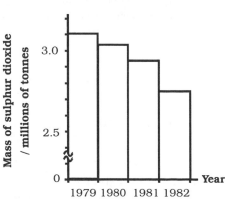

(a) Describe the trend shown by the bar graph.

(b) Suggest **one** reason for this trend.

(c) Sulphur dioxide can also be produced from burning petrol.

 (i) Name **two** other pollutants which can be found in car exhaust fumes.

 (ii) Describe how each gas is produced.

15. The following graphs show how the concentrations of some gases in car exhaust fumes vary with the air to fuel ratio of the mixture which is burned in the engine.

(a) Suggest why the carbon monoxide concentration approaches zero as the air to fuel ratio increases.

(b) Many car engines use an air to fuel ratio of 13.

Which of the gases has the highest concentration in car exhaust fumes using this air to fuel ratio?

(c) Use the information from the graphs to give the advantage of increasing the air to fuel ratio from 18 to 20.

16. Nitrogen oxides and carbon monoxide are polluting gases which are present in the exhaust mixtures from petrol engines.

(a) Explain the presence in car exhaust gases of

(i) nitrogen oxides,

(ii) carbon monoxide.

(b) In a catalytic converter, nitrogen oxides can react with carbon monoxide to form two non-toxic gases.

Suggest the names of these gases.

17. The table shows the percentage of energy consumed in the world from various sources in 1987.

Nuclear	Hydro electric	Gas	Coal	Oil
5	7	19	29	40

(a) Draw a **bar graph** to show this information.

(b) What percentage of World energy consumption in 1987 came from fossil fuels?

18. The small carbon dioxide cylinders which are used to make fizzy drinks can also provide a supply of the gas for experiments.

Carbon dioxide is denser than air.

(a) Identify the most suitable arrangement for collecting a sample of carbon dioxide.

(b) Explain why each of the other arrangements is less suitable than the arrangement chosen in part (a).

19. When sodium hydrogen carbonate (bicarbonate of soda) is heated strongly, it decomposes.

You have to carry out an experiment to prove that carbon dioxide and water vapour are produced.

Draw a labelled diagram of the apparatus which you would use to show how the experiment could be carried out.

20. Natural gas is readily available in the laboratory.
    To burn the gas, it is bubbled through water to monitor the flow rate, then
    passed through lumps of calcium chloride to dry it.

    Copy and complete a labelled diagram to show the arrangement you would use to
    do this.

21. A group of pupils undertook a project on acid rain. They designed the following
    apparatus to compare the amount of sulphur dioxide released from samples of
    different solid fuels. The sulphur dioxide changed the orange sodium dichromate
    solution to a green colour.

    (a) Droplets of water were always detected in the U-tube.

    What does this indicate about solid fuels?

    (b) Suggest a reason why the pupils designed the apparatus with **more than
    one** test tube of sodium dichromate solution.

    (c) Suggest a reason why the oxygen is bubbled through liquid paraffin before
    entering the combustion tube.

22. Pyrolysis can be used to convert waste plastics into useful products.
   In this process, the plastics are decomposed by heating in the absence of air.

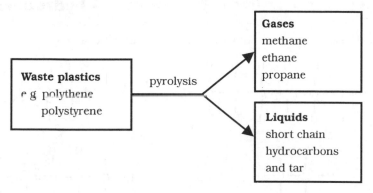

(a) Suggest why air must be absent during pyrolysis.

(b) Copy and complete the diagram to show how a sample of the products of
    pyrolysis can be collected with the liquids separate from the gases.

    Normal laboratory apparatus should be used and clearly labelled.

    No gas should be allowed to escape.

23. The first bicycle lamps were not electric. A hydrocarbon gas called acetylene was
   burned to produce the light.

   The acetylene gas was made by adding water to a solid called calcium carbide.

   Acetylene gas is insoluble in water.

   (a) Name the two products which are formed when acetylene burns in a
       plentiful supply of oxygen.

   (b) Draw a diagram of the apparatus you would use to prepare and collect a gas
       jar of acetylene in your chemistry laboratory.

Exercise 2.2   Nomenclature and structure
- hydrocarbons

1. Give the systematic name for each of the following hydrocarbons.

    (a)

$$H-\overset{\overset{\displaystyle H}{|}}{\underset{\underset{\displaystyle H}{|}}{C}}-\overset{\overset{\displaystyle H}{|}}{\underset{\underset{\displaystyle H}{|}}{C}}-\overset{\overset{\displaystyle H}{|}}{\underset{\underset{\displaystyle H}{|}}{C}}-\overset{\overset{\displaystyle H}{|}}{\underset{\underset{\displaystyle H}{|}}{C}}-\overset{\overset{\displaystyle H}{|}}{\underset{\underset{\displaystyle H}{|}}{C}}-\overset{\overset{\displaystyle H}{|}}{\underset{\underset{\displaystyle H}{|}}{C}}-H$$

    (b)

$$H-\overset{\overset{\displaystyle H}{|}}{\underset{\underset{\displaystyle H}{|}}{C}}-\overset{\overset{\displaystyle H}{|}}{\underset{\underset{\displaystyle H}{|}}{C}}=C\overset{\displaystyle H}{\underset{\displaystyle H}{{}}}$$

    (c)

$$H-\overset{\overset{\displaystyle H}{|}}{\underset{\underset{\displaystyle |}{|}}{C}}-\overset{\overset{\displaystyle H}{|}}{\underset{\underset{\displaystyle |}{|}}{C}}-H$$
$$H-\overset{}{\underset{\underset{\displaystyle H}{|}}{C}}-\overset{}{\underset{\underset{\displaystyle H}{|}}{C}}-H$$

    (d)

$$H-\overset{\overset{\displaystyle H}{|}}{\underset{\underset{\displaystyle H}{|}}{C}}-\overset{\overset{\displaystyle H}{|}}{\underset{\underset{\displaystyle H}{|}}{C}}-\overset{\overset{\displaystyle H}{|}}{C}=\overset{\overset{\displaystyle H}{|}}{\underset{\underset{\displaystyle H}{|}}{C}}-\overset{\overset{\displaystyle H}{|}}{\underset{\underset{\displaystyle H}{|}}{C}}-H$$

    (e) $CH_3-CH_2-CH_2-CH_2-CH_3$

    (f) $CH_3-CH=CH-CH_3$

    (g)

$$\begin{array}{ccc} & CH_2-CH_2 & \\ CH_2 & & CH_2 \\ & CH_2-CH_2 & \end{array}$$

2. For each of the following molecules

    (a) methane   (b) propene

    (c) cyclopentane   (d) butane

    (e) pent-1-ene   (f) hex-2-ene

    (i) draw the **full** structural formula,

    (ii) draw a **shortened** structural formula.

3. Give the systematic name for each of the following hydrocarbons.

    (a) $CH_3-\overset{}{\underset{\underset{\displaystyle CH_3}{|}}{CH}}-CH_2-CH_2-CH_3$

    (b) $CH_3-\overset{}{\underset{\underset{\displaystyle CH_3}{|}}{CH}}-\overset{}{\underset{\underset{\displaystyle CH_3}{|}}{CH}}-CH_3$

    (c) $CH_3-CH_2-\overset{\overset{\displaystyle CH_3}{|}}{\underset{\underset{\underset{\underset{\displaystyle CH_3}{|}}{CH_2}}{|}}{CH}}$

    (d) $CH_3-\overset{\overset{\displaystyle CH_3}{|}}{\underset{\underset{\displaystyle CH_3}{|}}{C}}-CH_2-CH_3$

4. Draw a shortened structural formula for each of the following hydrocarbons.
    (a) 3-ethylhexane
    (b) 2,2,4-trimethylpentane
    (c) 3-ethyl,2-methylpentane
    (d) pent-1,3-diene

5. State the molecular formula for each of the following hydrocarbons.
    (a) octane
    (b) hexene
    (c) cyclohexane
    (d) the straight-chain alkane with 12 carbon atoms per molecule
    (e) the straight-chain alkene with 10 carbon atoms per molecule
    (f) the cycloalkane with 8 carbon atoms per molecule

6. The full structural formulae below represent two members of a homologous
    series of compounds called the cycloalkenes.

    cyclobutene   **cyclohexene**

    (a) What is the general formula for the cycloalkene series?
    (b) Draw the full structural formula for the cycloalkene with five carbon atoms.

7. (a) Explain what is meant by a homologous series.
    (b) In each of the following lists of hydrocarbons identify the one which is in a
         different homologous series from the others.
         (i) ethane, butene, methane, octane
         (ii) C_3H_8, CH_4, C_7H_{14}, $C_{12}H_{26}$
         (iii) C_2H_4, C_6H_{12}, CH_4, C_4H_8

8. A pupil carried out a study with three organic compounds. All are members of a homologous series called alkanals.

Molecule	Structure
A	H—C—H ‖ O
B	H | H–C—C—H | ‖ H O
C	H H | | H–C—C—C—H | | ‖ H H O

Give a general formula for the alkanal series of organic compounds.

9. One of the first anaesthetics to be used was chloroform ($CHCl_3$).

The table shows the anaesthetic effect of methane and some chlorine compounds (like chloroform) which are based on methane.

Compound	Anaesthetic effect
CH_4	none
CH_3Cl	weak
CH_2Cl_2	moderate
$CHCl_3$	strong

(a) Using the information in the table, what general statement can be made about the compounds and their anaesthetic effect?

(b) Draw the full structural formula for $CHCl_3$.

10. The boiling points of some alkanes are given in the table below.

Alkane	Boiling point / K
methane	109
ethane	185
propane	231
butane	273
hexane	342

(a) Draw a **bar graph** to show this information.

(b) Use your graph to estimate the boiling point of pentane.

(c) You now have information about six alkanes, including pentane. Name the alkanes which are liquids at 250 K.

11. Here is some information about a series of compounds called alkynes.

Number of carbon atoms	Formula mass
2	26
3	40
4	54
5	68

(a) Draw a **bar graph** to show this information.

(b) Using either the information in the table or your bar graph, state the formula mass of the alkyne with 6 carbon atoms.

(c) From the information in the table, state the formula for the alkyne with 2 carbon atoms.

12. Naphtha can be cracked to give a number of useful products. A typical result is shown in the table.

Product	Methane	Ethene	Propene	Petrol	Other products
% by mass	15	25	16	28	15

(a) Draw a **bar graph** to show this result.

(b) Name the family of hydrocarbons to which ethene and propene belong.

13. OCTANE NUMBERS

A way of grading types of petrol is to use "octane numbers". The higher the octane number, the more efficiently the petrol burns.

Some hydrocarbons were tested in an experimental car engine and were found to have octane numbers as shown.

Hydrocarbon	Octane Number
$H-\overset{\underset{\mid}{H}}{\underset{H}{C}}-\overset{\underset{\mid}{H}}{\underset{H}{C}}-\overset{\underset{\mid}{H}}{\underset{H}{C}}-\overset{\underset{\mid}{H}}{\underset{H}{C}}-\overset{\underset{\mid}{H}}{\underset{H}{C}}-\overset{\underset{\mid}{H}}{\underset{H}{C}}-\overset{\underset{\mid}{H}}{\underset{H}{C}}-H$ (straight chain, 7 carbons)	0
(7-carbon chain with CH_3 branch on second carbon)	22
(straight chain, 6 carbons)	25
(5-carbon chain with two CH_3 branches)	65
(6-carbon chain with CH_3 branch)	73
(5-carbon chain with three CH_3 branches)	100

(a) Name the hydrocarbon with an octane number of 25.

(b) State **two** features of the molecular structure which give a high octane number.

14. The hydrocarbons present in a mixture can be separated using chromatography. The mixture is vapourised and is then passed through a special column. Different hydrocarbons move through the column at different speeds. The following graph was obtained.

Increasing time to move through the column.

(a) Make **two** general statements linking the structure of the hydrocarbon with the length of time taken to pass through the column.

(b) Copy the graph and show with an arrow, the expected position for propane.

Exercise 2.3

Nomenclature and structure
- alkanols and alkanoic acids

1. Give the systematic name for each of the following alkanols.

    (a)
    $$CH_3-CH_2-OH$$

    (b)
    $$CH_3-\underset{\underset{\displaystyle OH}{|}}{CH}-CH_2-CH_3$$

    (c)
    $$HO-CH_2-CH_2-CH_3$$

    (d)
    $$CH_3-CH_2-CH_2-\underset{\underset{\displaystyle OH}{|}}{CH}-CH_3$$

2. Draw a shortened structural formula for each of the following alkanols.

    (a) methanol

    (b) hexan-2-ol

    (c) pentan-3-ol

    (d) dimethylbutan-1-ol

3. Give the systematic name for each of the following alkanoic acids.

    (a)
    $$\overset{\overset{\displaystyle O}{||}}{H-C}-OH$$

    (b)

4. Draw a shortened structural formula for each of the following acids.

    (a) ethanoic acid

    (b) pentanoic acid

    (c) hexanoic acid

Exercise 2.4

Nomenclature and structure
- esters

1. Name each of the following esters.

(a)

$$CH_3-\overset{\overset{\textstyle O}{\|}}{C}-O-CH_3$$

(b)

$$CH_3-O-\overset{\overset{\textstyle O}{\|}}{C}-H$$

(c)

$$CH_3-\overset{\overset{\textstyle O}{\|}}{C}-O-CH_2CH_2CH_3$$

(d)

$$H-\overset{\overset{\textstyle O}{\|}}{C}-O-CH_2CH_3$$

2. Draw a structural formula for each of the following esters.
    (a) ethyl ethanoate
    (b) propyl butanoate

3. For each of the following parent alkanols and alkanoic acids, name the ester which is formed and draw a structural formula.
    (a) ethanol / methanoic acid
    (b) methanol / propanoic acid

(c)

$$CH_3CH_2-OH\ /\quad CH_3-\overset{\overset{\textstyle O}{\|}}{C}-OH$$

(d)

$$CH_3CH_2CH_2-OH\ /\quad H-\overset{\overset{\textstyle O}{\|}}{C}-OH$$

4. For the breakdown of each of the following esters, name the products and draw their structural formulae.
    (a) ethyl propanoate
    (b) methyl ethanoate

(c)

$$CH_3CH_2-O-\overset{\overset{\textstyle O}{\|}}{C}-H$$

(d)

$$CH_3CH_2CH_2-\overset{\overset{\textstyle O}{\|}}{C}-O-CH_3$$

Exercise 2.5   Isomers

1. State whether each of the following pairs of molecules are
   A isomers   **B** **not** isomers.

(a)

(b)

(c)

(d)

(e)

(f)

(g)

```
        H                              H
        |                              |
      H-C-H                          H-C-H
    H       H                    H       H
    |       |                    |       |
  H-C   C   C-H                H-C   C   C-H
    |   |   |                    |   |   |
    H       H                    H       H
      H-C-H                          H-C-H
        |                              |
        H                              H
```

(h)

```
      H   H                     H   H   H
       \ /                      |   |   |
        C                     H-C - C - C-H
       / \                      |   |   |
      C — C                     H   H   H
     /     \
    H       H
```

(i)

```
    H   H                     H   H
     \ /                      |   |        H
      C       H   H         H-C - C - C   /
      ‖       |   |           |   |   ‖
      C - C - C-H             H   H   C
     /    |   |                      / \
    H     H   H                     H   H
```

(j)

```
    H   H                     H           H
     \ /                      |           |
      C       H   H         H-C - C = C - C-H
      ‖       |   |           |           |
      C - C - C-H             H   H   H   H
     /    |   |
    H     H   H
```

(k)

```
      H   H                     H   Cl
      |   |                      |   |
   Cl-C - C-Cl                 H-C - C-H
      |   |                      |   |
      H   H                     Cl   H
```

(l)

```
     Cl  Cl                    Cl   H
      |   |                     |   |
    H-C - C-H                Cl-C - C-H
      |   |                     |   |
      H   H                     H   H
```

2. Draw a shortened structural formula for each of the following hydrocarbons and give the systematic name.
   (a) the **three** isomers of C_5H_{12}
   (b) the **three** straight-chain isomers of cyclohexane

3. **Two** isomeric straight-chain alcohols, each having four carbon atoms, are known.

   Draw a structural formula for each of these alcohols.

4. (a) Draw structural formulae for the **two** esters which are isomers of propanoic acid.
   (b) Name each of the esters.

Intermediate 2 Chemistry

Exercise 2.6   Reactions of carbon compounds

1. (a) Explain what is meant by
        (i)   a saturated hydrocarbon,   (ii)   an unsaturated hydrocarbon.
    (b) Consider this list of hydrocarbons:
            butane,   ethene,   octane,   methane,   butene
        Name the hydrocarbons which are
        (i)   saturated,   (ii)   unsaturated

2.

    (a) Draw the full structural formula for substance **X**?
    (b) What name is given to this type of chemical reaction?
    (c) Name the product of the reaction of C_2H_4 with H_2.

3. C_3H_6 + Br_2 → $C_3H_6Br_2$

    (a) Is the hydrocarbon C_3H_6 saturated or unsaturated?
    (b) What name is given to the above type of chemical reaction?
    (c) Draw the full structural formula for the product of the reaction.

4. White spirit (turpentine substitute) is used as paint thinner. Both saturated and
    unsaturated hydrocarbons are present in white spirit.
    Describe how you would test white spirit to show that it contains unsaturated
    hydrocarbons.

5. The full structural formulae below represent two members of a homologous
    series of compounds called the cycloalkenes.

        cyclobutene   **cyclohexene**

    Both react with bromine solution.
    Write the molecular formulae for each of the compounds formed.

6. Three different hydrocarbons were treated with bromine solution. Each of the hydrocarbons contained six carbon atoms. The results are shown.

Formula	Hydrocarbon	Effect on bromine
C_6H_{12}	A	decolourises quickly
C_6H_{14}	B	no immediate change
C_6H_{12}	C	no immediate change

Give the names and draw possible structures for **A**, **B** and **C**.

7. Terpenes are important in the perfume industry. One example is terpinolene, an unsaturated hydrocarbon with the molecular formula $C_{10}H_{16}$. The structural formula is shown.

(a) What is meant by an unsaturated hydrocarbon?

(b) Write the molecular formula for the product of the complete reaction of terpinolene with bromine.

8.

$$\text{chloroethane} \xleftarrow{\quad H_2 \quad} \textbf{X} \xrightarrow{\quad \textbf{Y} \quad} \text{1,2-dichloroethane}$$

(a) Draw the full structural formula for compound **X**.

(b) Name reagent **Y**.

9. (a) Draw the full structural formula for the product when each of the following hydrocarbons is bubbled through bromine solution.

(i)

(ii)

(b) What name is given to the kind of reaction which takes place?

10. Some doctors recommend thar we eat unsaturated vegetable oils rather than saturated oils. There is evidence to suggest that this reduces the risk of heart disease.

Each oil is given an "iodine value". This is the volume of iodine solution which is decolourised by 10 cm^3 of oil.

You are given the following apparatus.

measuring cylinder   vegetable oil (colourless)   beaker   syringe (for iodine solution)   iodine solution (brown)   stirring rod

Suggest how you would use this apparatus to find the iodine value of the oil.

11. There are many chemical compounds containing the elements carbon, hydrogen and oxygen. The extended structural formulae for three such compounds are shown.

A
```
    H   H   H
    |   |   |
H—C—C—C—O—H
    |   |   |
    H   H   H
```

B
```
    H   H   O
    |   |   ||
H—C—C—C—H
    |   |
    H   H
```

C
```
    H   O   H
    |   ||  |
H—C—C—C—H
    |       |
    H       H
```

A class carried out experiments with each of the compounds. One pupil's results are shown.

Compound	Reaction with sodium	Effect on acidified potassium permanganate	Flammable or not flammable
A	gas produced	goes colourless	flammable
B	no reaction	goes colourless	flammable
C	no reaction	none	flammable

(a) From the results, what general statement can be made about all three compounds?

(b) From the results, describe how to distinguish **A** from **B**.

(c) Predict what will happen when acidified potassium permanganate is added to a compound with the structure shown.

```
    H   O   H   H
    |   ||  |   |
H—C—C—C—C—H
    |       |   |
    H       H   H
```

12. The OXO Process involves the reaction between an alkene and synthesis gas (a mixture of carbon monoxide and hydrogen).

   The product is an alcohol with one carbon atom more than the alkene.

$$CH_3-CH=CH_2 \ + \ CO \ + \ 2H_2 \quad \rightarrow \qquad CH_3-\underset{\underset{CH_2OH}{|}}{CH}-CH_3$$

   (a) Draw the formula for an alkene which would give the following alcohol.

$$CH_3-\underset{\underset{CH_2OH}{|}}{CH}-CH_2-CH_3$$

   (b) Draw the formula for the alcohol which would be obtained from ethene.

13. Alkanes can be made by the reaction of sodium with iodoalkanes.

   This is called the Wurtz synthesis.

   For example, ethane can be made from iodomethane.

$$H-\underset{\underset{H}{|}}{\overset{\overset{H}{|}}{C}}-I \ + \ 2Na \ + \ I-\underset{\underset{H}{|}}{\overset{\overset{H}{|}}{C}}-H \quad \rightarrow \quad H-\underset{\underset{H}{|}}{\overset{\overset{H}{|}}{C}}-\underset{\underset{H}{|}}{\overset{\overset{H}{|}}{C}}-H \ + \ 2NaI$$

   (a) Name the alkane which forms when sodium reacts with iodoethane.
   (b) Two different iodoalkanes are used to make propane.
       Name the two iodoalkanes.
   (c) The Wurtz synthesis can also be used to make cycloalkanes.
       Draw the full structural formula of the compound which could be used to make cyclobutane.

14. The following reaction shows what happens when an alkene reacts with ozone.

$$H-\underset{\underset{H}{|}}{\overset{\overset{H}{|}}{C}}-\underset{\underset{H}{|}}{\overset{\overset{H}{|}}{C}}-\overset{\overset{H}{|}}{C}=\underset{\underset{H}{|}}{C}-\overset{\overset{H}{|}}{C}-H \ + \ ozone \ \rightarrow \ H-\underset{\underset{H}{|}}{\overset{\overset{H}{|}}{C}}-\underset{\underset{H}{|}}{\overset{\overset{H}{|}}{C}}-\overset{\overset{H}{|}}{C}=O \ + \ O=\underset{\underset{H}{|}}{C}-\overset{\overset{H}{|}}{C}-H$$

   (a) Draw the full structural formulae of the products you would expect from the following reaction.

$$H-\underset{\underset{H}{|}}{\overset{\overset{H}{|}}{C}}-\overset{\overset{H}{|}}{C}=\underset{}{C}-\underset{\underset{H}{|}}{\overset{\overset{H}{|}}{C}}-\underset{\underset{H}{|}}{\overset{\overset{H}{|}}{C}}-\underset{\underset{H}{|}}{\overset{\overset{H}{|}}{C}}-H \ + \ ozone \ \rightarrow$$

   (b) Ozonolysis of another molecule gives only **one** product.
       Draw the full structural formula of an alkene which would react in this way.

15. Alkenes can be synthesised by reacting a carbonyl compound with a phosphorus compound.

$$
\begin{array}{c}
R_1 \\
| \\
C=O \\
| \\
R_2
\end{array}
+
\begin{array}{c}
\quad C_6H_5 \ R_3 \\
\quad\ \ | \quad\ | \\
C_6H_5-P=C \\
\quad\ \ | \quad\ | \\
\quad C_6H_5 \ R_4
\end{array}
\rightarrow
\begin{array}{c}
R_1 \quad R_3 \\
| \quad\ \ | \\
C=C \\
| \quad\ \ | \\
R_2 \quad R_4
\end{array}
+
\begin{array}{c}
\quad\ C_6H_5 \\
\quad\ \ | \\
C_6H_5-P=O \\
\quad\ \ | \\
\quad\ C_6H_5
\end{array}
$$

R is a shorthand way of writing a hydrogen atom or an alkane with one hydrogen atom removed,

i.e. $-R$ could be $-H$, $\quad -CH_3$, $\quad -C_2H_5$, $\quad -C_3H_7$, etc.

(a) Draw the structural formula for the alkene formed in the following reaction.

$$
\begin{array}{c}
CH_3 \\
| \\
C=O \\
| \\
CH_3
\end{array}
+
\begin{array}{c}
\quad C_6H_5 \ H \\
\quad\ \ | \quad\ | \\
C_6H_5-P=C \\
\quad\ \ | \quad\ | \\
\quad C_6H_5 \ CH_3
\end{array}
\rightarrow
$$

(b) Draw the structural formula for the carbonyl compound that would be used to make ethene.

16. Organic chemistry has a number of rules that can help to predict the products of a reaction.

The equation shows what happens when an ionic compound in solution is added to an alkene.

$$
\begin{array}{c}
H \quad\ H \\
| \quad\ \ | \\
C=C \\
| \quad\ \ | \\
H \quad CH_3
\end{array}
+ \ H^+Br^-(aq) \ \rightarrow
\begin{array}{c}
\quad\ \ H \quad\ H \\
\quad\ \ | \quad\ \ | \\
H-C-C-Br \\
\quad\ \ | \quad\ \ | \\
\quad\ \ H \quad CH_3
\end{array}
$$

The positive ion adds on to the double-bonded carbon atom which has the greater number of hydrogen atoms bonded to it.

(a)

$$
\begin{array}{c}
H \quad CH_3 \\
| \quad\ \ | \\
C=C \\
| \quad\ \ | \\
H \quad CH_3
\end{array}
+ \ HO^-Cl^+(aq) \ \rightarrow \quad Product
$$

Draw the full structural formula for the product in the above reaction.

(b) Draw the full structural formula for an isomer of butene which could **not** be used to demonstrate the above rule.

Exercise 2.7 Cracking

1. An example of cracking is shown in the equation below.

$$C_8H_{18} \quad \rightarrow \quad C_6H_{14} \quad + \quad \underline{\quad}$$
$$\textbf{A} \qquad\qquad \textbf{B} \qquad\qquad\qquad \textbf{C}$$

   (a) Explain what is meant by cracking.

   (b) Draw a labelled diagram to show how the cracking of hydrocarbon **A** can be carried out in the laboratory. Show how the gas **C** can be collected.

   (c) Name a catalyst that can be used to speed up the reaction.

   (d) Name the hydrocarbons **A** and **B**.

   (e) What is the formula and the name of **C**?

   (f) Describe an experiment which can be used to distinguish between **A** and **C**.

   (g) Explain why cracking is one of the important processes carried out in an oil refinery.

2. (a) The hydrocarbon has no immediate effect of bromine water. What does this indicate?

   (b) The hydrocarbon is used in the following apparatus.

porcelain chips

liquid hydrocarbon on ceramic wool

gas

water

heat

   (i) The gas collected rapidly decolourises bromine water. Why is this?

   (ii) Name the chemical reaction occurring in the heated tube.

   (iii) As soon as heating is stopped what precaution must be taken? Explain why this is necessary.

3. The cracking of paraffin can be carried out in the laboratory using strong heat. A mixture of saturated and unsaturated products is obtained.

   (a) What effect would a suitable catalyst have on the amount of heat needed to crack paraffin?

   (b) Explain why cracking produces a mixture of saturated and unsaturated products.

4. Gasoline and gas oil are two of the fractions which can be obtained from crude oil. Gas oil can be cracked to give more gasoline.

   (a) State **two** ways in which the molecules produced by cracking can be different from the molecules in gas oil.

   (b) The chart shows the fractions supplied by distilling crude oil and the demand for these fractions.

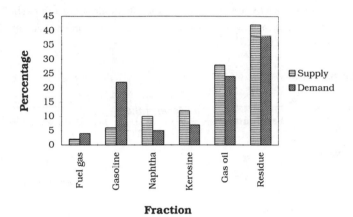

Explain why gas oil is cracked to produce gasoline.

Exercise 2.8   Ethanol

1. Alcohol for drinks can be made from carbohydrates.
   (a) Name the type of reaction which takes place.
   (b) Name **three** sources of carbohydrates for the production of an alcoholic drink.
   (c) Describe briefly how to obtain a sample of alcohol from carbohydrates.
   (d) Give **two** ways in which alcoholic drinks, taken in excess, can damage the body.

2. **Carbohydrate**

   (a) (i) Name gas **X** .
       (ii) What kind of substance, present in yeast, acts as a catalyst for the reaction?
       (iii) Name the alcohol produced by this process.
   (b) Explain why there is a limit to the concentration of ethanol obtained in this reaction.
   (c) Name process **Y**.

3. Ethanol can be prepared in industry by an addition reaction between steam and hydrocarbon **X**.

$$ \mathbf{X} \;+\; H_2O \;\;\rightarrow\;\; H-\underset{\underset{H}{|}}{\overset{\overset{H}{|}}{C}}-\underset{\underset{H}{|}}{\overset{\overset{H}{|}}{C}}-OH $$

   (a) Name hydrocarbon **X**.
   (b) Give another name for this type of reaction.

4. Ethanol can be used to make ethene.

$$ H-\underset{\underset{H}{|}}{\overset{\overset{H}{|}}{C}}-\underset{\underset{H}{|}}{\overset{\overset{H}{|}}{C}}-OH \;\;\rightarrow\;\; \underset{\underset{H}{|}}{\overset{\overset{H}{|}}{C}}=\underset{\underset{H}{|}}{\overset{\overset{H}{|}}{C}} $$

   (a) Name the type of reaction which takes place.
   (b) Draw a structural formula for the compound which is produced when propanol is involved in this type of reaction.

Exercise 2.9   Making and breaking esters

1.

$$CH_3-\overset{\overset{\textstyle O}{\|}}{C}-O-\underset{\underset{\textstyle CH_3}{|}}{CH}-C_2H_5$$

(a) Give the systematic names of the carboxylic acid and the alkanol which, when warmed with concentrated sulphuric acid, react to form the above ester.

(b) Unless the ester is removed from the reaction mixture as it forms, 100% conversion of reactants to ester is never achieved.

Give the reason for this.

2. Preparation of ethyl ethanoate from ethanoic acid and ethanol results in an equilibrium mixture.

$$CH_3-\overset{\overset{\textstyle O}{\|}}{C}-OH \;+\; C_2H_5-OH \;\rightleftharpoons\; CH_3-\overset{\overset{\textstyle O}{\|}}{C}-O-C_2H_5 \;+\; H_2O$$

MIXTURE
pour into water

SOLUBLE
X

INSOLUBLE
Y

(a) Name the kind of reaction which takes place in the preparation.

(b) Name the substances present at **X** and **Y**.

3. The artificial sweetener, aspartame, is a dimethyl ester of the compound shown.

$$HO-\overset{\overset{\textstyle CH_2}{|}}{\underset{\underset{\textstyle O}{\|}}{C}}-CH-NH-\overset{\overset{\textstyle O}{\|}}{C}-\underset{\underset{\textstyle}{}}{CH}-CH_2-\overset{\overset{\textstyle O}{\|}}{C}-OH$$

Draw a structural formula for aspartame.

4. (a) Salicylic acid occurs in the form of its methyl ester as a constituent of oil of wintergreen, in the North American health plant, Gaultheria Procumbens. The formula for salicylic acid may be represented:

Draw a structural formula for the ester formed when the acid group reacts with methanol.

(b) Acetylsalicylic acid is widely used as a pain killer under its commercial name "Aspirin". The formula may be written as:

(i) What is meant by hydrolysis?

(ii) Draw structural formulae for the products of the hydrolysis of the ester group in Aspirin.

(iii) Suggest why Aspirin tablets which are kept for many months, especially in hot and humid climates, often smell of vinegar (ethanoic acid).

5. Poly(ethenol) is a recently developed plastic which is soluble in water. It is made from another polymer.

poly(ethenol)

(a) Draw a structural formula for the acid produced in the step shown.

(b) Name the type of reaction taking place.

Exercise 2.10   Plastics and synthetic fibres

1. Plastics are synthetic materials; wood is a natural material.
   (a) Explain the difference between a natural and a synthetic material.
   (b) What raw material is used to make most plastics and synthetic fibres?
   (c) Give **two** examples of a synthetic fibres.

2. The following is a list of plastics:

   polystyrene, polythene, polyvinyl chloride (PVC), perspex, melamine, bakelite
   (a) Copy and complete the following table by matching each plastic with the appropriate uses.

Plastic	Uses
	washing-up bowls, waste-bin liners
	window frames, pipes, guttering
	plates, tumblers
	safety screens, spectacle lenses
	electric plugs and switches
	packaging, ceiling tiles

   (b) Give **one** reason why each plastic is used in the particular way.

3. Many items which were once made of other materials are now made of plastic. However, plastics can also have disadvantages.
   (a) State **two** reasons why plastics are now preferred for pipes and guttering.
   (b) (i) Why are the fumes from burning plastics dangerous?
       (ii) State **one** other problem which can arise from the use of plastics.

4. Explain the purpose of each of the following.
   (a) the Teflon skin on some frying pans
   (b) the PVC skin on some wallpapers
   (c) the PVC covering of electric wire

5. Thermosetting plastics have different properties from thermoplastics.
   (a) Explain what is meant by
       (i) a thermosetting plastic,
       (ii) a thermoplastic.
   (b) State which type is used to make
       (i) electric plugs and switches,
       (ii) washing-up bowls.

6. A plastic bottle has the following label.

> **NON-BIODEGRADABLE**
> To dispose of this plastic bottle,
> simply fill with hot water. When soft,
> empty and flatten.

(a) Explain what is meant by non-biodegradable.

(b) What type of plastic is suggested by the instructions on the label?

7. (a) State what is meant by a **biodegradable** plastic.

(b) Most plastics are **not** biodegradable.

   (i) Why might this be an advantage?

   (ii) Why might this be a disadvantage?

8. Kevlar, poly(ethenol) and Biopol are recently developed polymers with important properties.

Give **one** property associated with each polymer.

9. The structures of three monomers used to make plastics **A**, **B** and **C** are shown.

All the plastics burn or smoulder to give off toxic fumes.

Identify the plastic(s) which can give off

(a) carbon monoxide,

(b) hydrogen chloride,

(c) hydrogen cyanide.

Exercise 2.11   Making polymers (i)

1. Plastics are examples of polymers. Different monomers are used to make different plastics.
   (a) Explain what is meant by
       (i) a monomer,
       (ii) a polymer.
   (b) Name the process which takes place when a polymer is made from a monomer.
   (c) Name the polymer which is made from
       (i) styrene,
       (ii) propene,
       (iii) vinyl chloride.
   (d) What is common to the structures of all of the above monomers?
   (e) The above monomers are obtained from the same raw material.
       (i) What is this raw material?
       (ii) Name the **two** processes by which the monomers are obtained from the raw material.

2. Poly(ethene) is a widely used polymer.
   (a) (i) Name the monomer unit.
       (ii) Draw the full structural formula for the monomer unit.
   (b) Draw the structure of part of a poly(ethene) chain to show how **three** monomer units have joined together.

3. Polyvinylidene chloride is an addition polymer. It is added to carpet fabrics to reduce flammability. It is made from the monomer vinylidene chloride.
   Part of the polymer chain is shown.

$$-\overset{\overset{\displaystyle H}{|}}{\underset{\underset{\displaystyle H}{|}}{C}}-\overset{\overset{\displaystyle Cl}{|}}{\underset{\underset{\displaystyle Cl}{|}}{C}}-\overset{\overset{\displaystyle H}{|}}{\underset{\underset{\displaystyle H}{|}}{C}}-\overset{\overset{\displaystyle Cl}{|}}{\underset{\underset{\displaystyle Cl}{|}}{C}}-\overset{\overset{\displaystyle H}{|}}{\underset{\underset{\displaystyle H}{|}}{C}}-\overset{\overset{\displaystyle Cl}{|}}{\underset{\underset{\displaystyle Cl}{|}}{C}}-$$

   (a) What is meant by an **addition** polymer?
   (b) How many repeating units are shown ?
   (c) Draw the full structural formula of the vinylidene chloride monomer.

4. Poly(propene) is used to make many kitchen items.
   (a) Name the monomer unit from which poly(propene) is made.
   (b) Draw a structural formula for the monomer unit.
   (c) Draw the structure of part of a poly(propene) chain to show how **three** monomer units have joined together.

5. Orlon is a synthetic fibre made from monomers with the following structure.

$$
\begin{array}{ccc}
H & & H \\
| & & | \\
C & = & C \\
| & & | \\
H & & CN \\
\end{array}
$$

(a) Draw the structure of the repeating unit in Orlon.

(b) Draw the structure of part of the Orlon chain to show how **three** monomer units have joined together.

6. Polyvinyl chloride (PVC) is a well known polymer.

$$
\begin{array}{ccccccccc}
 & H & H & H & H & H & H & H & H \\
 & | & | & | & | & | & | & | & | \\
-C & -C & -C & -C & -C & -C & -C & -C & - \\
 & | & | & | & | & | & | & | & | \\
 & Cl & H & Cl & H & Cl & H & Cl & H \\
\end{array}
$$

(a) How many repeating units are shown?

(b) Draw the full structural formula for the monomer unit.

(c) What type of polymerisation occurs in the formation of this polymer?

7. PTFE is an addition polymer made from tetrafluoroethene.

(a) What does PTFE stand for?

(b) Draw the full structural formula for tetrafluoroethene.

(c) Draw the structure of part of a PTFE chain to show how **three** monomer units have joined together.

8.

CH_2-CH_3 $CH=CH_2$

ethylbenzene   **phenylethene (styrene)**

(a) Describe a test which could be used to distinguish ethylbenzene from styrene.

(b) Which of the above molecules would undergo polymerisation?

(c) What type of polymerisation would occur?

(d) Draw the structure of part of the polymer chain to show how **three** monomer units have joined together.

9. Perspex is as transparent as glass but does not break easily. This polymer is therefore used to make safety screens, spectacle lenses, and aeroplane windows. The following diagram shows part of a molecule of perspex.

$$
\begin{array}{ccccccc}
& \text{H} & & \text{CH}_3 \ \ \text{H} & & \text{CH}_3 \ \ \text{H} & & \text{CH}_3 \ \ \text{H} & & \text{CH}_3 \\
& | & & | \ \ \ \ \ | & & | \ \ \ \ \ | & & | \ \ \ \ \ | & & | \\
-\text{C} & - & \text{C} - \text{C} & - & \text{C} - \text{C} & - & \text{C} - \text{C} & - & \text{C} - \\
& | & & | \ \ \ \ \ | & & | \ \ \ \ \ | & & | \ \ \ \ \ | & & | \\
& \text{COOCH}_3 & & \text{H} \ \ \ \text{COOCH}_3 \ \ \text{H} & & \text{COOCH}_3 \ \ \text{H} & & \text{COOCH}_3 \ \ \text{H}
\end{array}
$$

(a) Draw the structure of the repeating unit in perspex.

(b) Draw a structural formula for the monomer used to make perspex.

10. Poly(butene) is used to make pipes which carry hot water under pressure. This is very useful in plumbing and underfloor heating. Poly(butene) is made using but-1-ene monomer.

$$
\begin{array}{cccc}
\text{H} & \text{H} & \text{H} & \text{H} \\
| & | & | & | \\
\text{C}={} & \text{C} - \text{C} - \text{C} - \text{H} \\
| & | & | & | \\
\text{H} & & \text{H} & \text{H}
\end{array}
$$

but-1-ene

(a) Draw the structure of part of the poly(butene) chain which is formed by **three** monomer units linking together.

(b) But-1-ene has a number of isomers.
Draw a strucural formula for an isomer which

(i) could be used to form a polymer,

(ii) could **not** be used to form a polymer.

11. Part of the structure of a polymer molecule is shown.

$$
\begin{array}{cccccccccccc}
\text{H} & \text{Cl} & \text{H} & \text{H} & \text{H} & \text{Cl} & \text{H} & \text{H} & \text{H} & \text{Cl} & \text{H} & \text{H} \\
| & | & | & | & | & | & | & | & | & | & | & | \\
-\text{C} & -\text{C}=\text{C} & -\text{C} & -\text{C} & -\text{C}=\text{C} & -\text{C} & -\text{C} & -\text{C}=\text{C} & -\text{C}- \\
| & & | & & | & | & & | & | & & | \\
\text{H} & & \text{H} & \text{H} & & \text{H} & \text{H} & & \text{H}
\end{array}
$$

(a) Draw the structure of the repeating unit.

(b) Describe a chemical test which could be used to distinguish between this polymer and poly(ethene).

13. Bucrylate is an ester which is used in surgery for repairing torn tissue.

$$
\begin{array}{cc}
\text{H} & \text{CN} \\
| & | \\
\text{H}-\text{C}=\text{C} & -\text{C}-\text{O}-\text{CH}_2-\text{CH}-\text{CH}_3 \\
& \parallel \ \ \ \ \ \ \ \ \ \ \ \ | \\
& \text{O} \ \ \ \ \ \ \ \ \ \ \text{CH}_3
\end{array}
$$

It instantaneously polymerises when it comes into contact with ionic solutions.

(a) What type of polymerisation will bucrylate undergo?

(b) Draw the structure of the repeating unit in polybucrylate.

Exercise 2.12

1. Terylene is a synthetic condensation polymer. It is made from the two monomers shown .

    | **A** | is |

    | **B** | is |

    These monomer units join in the order:

    (a) Name the small molecule which is usually a product in a condensation reaction.

    (b) Draw the structure of part of the polymer showing how **two** of each of the monomer units have joined together.

    (c) Name **one** other synthetic condensation polymer.

2. Polymerisation occurs between the following two compounds.

    $H_2N-CH_2CH_2-NH_2$ **A**

    $HO-\overset{\overset{O}{\|}}{C}$—⬡—$\overset{\overset{O}{\|}}{C}-OH$ **B**

    (a) To which classes of organic compounds do **A** and **B** belong?

    (b) Which type of polymerisation occurs between these two compounds?

    (c) Draw the structure of part of the polymer chain showing **two** of each monomer unit linked together.

3. Kevlar is a polymer which, weight for weight, is five times as strong as steel. Part of the molecular structure is shown.

    (a) Draw the structure of the repeating unit.

    (b) Draw a structural formula for each of the monomers used to make Kevlar.

    (c) What type of polymer is Kevlar?

4. The diagram shows part of the structure of a polymer molecule.

$$-\overset{\overset{\displaystyle O}{\|}}{C}-(CH_2)_4-\overset{\overset{\displaystyle O}{\|}}{C}-O-(CH_2)_2-O-\overset{\overset{\displaystyle O}{\|}}{C}-(CH_2)_4-\overset{\overset{\displaystyle O}{\|}}{C}-O-(CH_2)_2-O-$$

(a) Draw the structure of the repeating unit.

(b) Draw a structural formula for each of the monomers used to make the polymer.

5. Caprolactam is an intermediate in the manufacture of nylon. The structure of caprolactam is:

(a) (i) In a polymeriser, water in catalytic amounts reacts with a small percentage of the caprolactam, opening the ring by hydrolysis and producing a molecule with two different functional groups.

Draw a structural formula for the molecule produced.

(ii) This molecule initiates a chain reaction with other caprolactam molecules. As a result, each ring is opened and the molecules join head to tail, to form a long chain molecule (nylon 6) which has the structure:

$$-\underset{H}{N}-(CH_2)_5-\underset{O}{\overset{\|}{C}}-\underset{H}{N}-(CH_2)_5-\underset{O}{\overset{\|}{C}}-\underset{H}{N}-(CH_2)_5-\underset{O}{\overset{\|}{C}}-$$

Draw the structure of the repeating unit of nylon 6.

(b) The structure of nylon 6,6 is:

$$-\underset{H}{N}-(CH_2)_6-\underset{H\ O}{N}-\overset{\|}{C}-(CH_2)_4-\overset{\|}{C}-\underset{O\ H}{N}-(CH_2)_6-\underset{H\ O}{N}-\overset{\|}{C}-(CH_2)_4-\overset{\|}{C}-$$

(i) Draw the structure of the repeating unit of nylon 6,6.

(ii) Draw structural formulae for the **two** monomers from which nylon 6,6 is made.

(iii) What type of condensation polymer is nylon 6,6?

6. BIOPOL-PHBV is a recently launched biodegradable polyester.

$$-O-\underset{\underset{CH_3}{|}}{CH}-CH_2-\underset{\overset{O}{||}}{C}-O-\underset{\underset{C_2H_5}{|}}{CH}-CH_2-\underset{\overset{O}{||}}{C}-O-\underset{\underset{CH_3}{|}}{CH}-CH_2-\underset{\overset{O}{||}}{C}-$$

The first step in the biodegradation of BIOPOL-PHBV involves hydrolysis of the ester linkages giving **two** similar compounds.

Draw a structural formula for each of these compounds.

7. Polylactic acid is a biodegradable polyester which can be made from lactic acid.

$$HO-\underset{\underset{CH_3}{|}}{\overset{\overset{H}{|}}{C}}-C\overset{\diagup O}{\diagdown OH} \qquad \textbf{lactic acid}$$

(a) Draw the structure of polylactic acid to show how **three** monomer units are joined together.

(b) Name the type of polymerisation which takes place.

Exercise 2.13   Carbohydrates

1. Starch and glucose are both carbohydrates.

    (a) Name the elements which are found in a carbohydrate.

    (b) Why are carbohydrates an important part of a balanced diet?

2. (a) A carbohydrate was tested as shown in the diagram below.

Test 1

**solution of carbohydrate
+Benedict's solution**

hot water

Test 2

iodine solution

carbohydrate

Result: No change in colour of
Benedict's solution.

Result: Iodine solution did not
change colour.

Suggest a name for the carbohydrate which was tested.

(b) A different carbohydrate was tested as shown below.

Test 3

**carbohydrate in water
+dilute hydrochloric acid**

hot water

Test 4

iodine solution

carbohydrate

Result: After the solution was
neutralised, Benedict's solution
gave an orange precipitate.

Result: Iodine solution turned
blue/black.

(i) Name the carbohydrate used in Tests 3 and 4.

(ii) Name the carbohydrate produced by the reaction in Test 3.

(iii) What kind of substance, present in saliva, could have been used in
place of the dilute hydrochloric acid to produce the same result as in
Test 3.

3. Glucose, sucrose and starch are all white solids.

Given an unlabelled sample of each, describe how you would discover which was which.

(Give the results of the tests that you would carry out.)

4. Carbohydrates supply the body with energy.

Explain why eating a Mars bar (containing glucose) just before a race might be of more value to a sportsman that eating bread (containing starch).

5. Many of the foods we eat contain starch. The starch molecules are hydrolysed in our bodies.

(a) Explain what is meant by hydrolysis.

(b) What is formed by the hydrolysis of starch?

(c) Why do foods containing glucose give us energy faster than starch foods?

6. A compound **X** is thought to be a carbohydrate. It is tested as follows.

Test 1   When burned in air, **X** produced CO_2 and H_2O

Test 2   When **X** is added to iodine solution, there is no change in colour.

Test 3   When **X** is warmed with Benedict's solution, there is no change in colour.

Test 4   After **X** has been heated with dilute acid, the product gives a positive Benedict's test.

(a) From Test 1 **alone**, explain whether it is reasonable to conclude that **X** is a carbohydrate.

(b) From Test 2 **alone**, what conclusion can be reached?

(c) From Test 3 **alone**, what conclusion can be reached?

(d)   (i)   In Test 4, what is happening to **X** when it reacts with acid?

(ii)   What name is given to this type of reaction?

7. A glucose molecule can be represented as shown.

(a) Use the representation to draw **three** units in the starch polymer chain.

(b) What type of polymerisation take place when starch is formed from glucose?

8. Bees collect nectar from flowers to make honey. The nectar contains sucrose which is broken down in the bees' bodies to give glucose and fructose.

(a) Name the family of compounds to which glucose and fructose belong.

(b) Name the type of substance in the bees' bodies which can break down sucrose.

(c) Describe the test you would use to show that honey contains glucose.

9. The enzyme hydrolysis of starch to produce glucose is normally carried out at a temperature around 40 °C.

   (a) (i) Would the reaction be speeded up by boiling?

   (ii) Explain your answer.

   (b) What type of substance could be used in place of the enzymes to hydrolyse starch at boiling point?

10. Some magicians use chemical reactions in their acts.

   In one such reaction, two colourless solutions, **A** and **B**, are added together. After a time delay, the colourless reaction mixture suddenly turns blue / black.

   (a) Name **two** substances which could have reacted together to give the blue / black colour.

   (b) To prepare for his act, a magician needed to know how the concentration of solution **A** affected the time it took for the colour to appear.
   He did four experiments, each with a different concentration of solution **A**. In each experiment, he measured the time it took for the blue / black colour to appear.

   State **two** factors which the magician had to keep the same in his experiments.

Exercise 2.14 — Proteins

1. (a) Give **one** reason why proteins are an essential part of a balanced diet.
   (b) What type of molecules are formed by the hydrolysis of proteins?
   (c) Name **four** elements found in all proteins.

2. Glycine is an amino acid with the following structure.

$$\underset{\underset{H}{|}}{H}-\overset{\overset{H}{|}}{N}-CH_2-\overset{\overset{O}{\|}}{C}-OH$$

   (a) Draw the structure of **three** repeating units in the polymer which would be formed from glycine.
   (b) What type of reaction would be taking place?

3. The diagram shows how amino acids are linked together in a protein.

$$-\overset{\overset{}{|}}{\underset{\underset{H}{|}}{N}}-CH_2-\overset{}{\underset{\underset{O}{\|}}{C}}-\overset{\overset{}{|}}{\underset{\underset{H}{|}}{N}}-\overset{\overset{CH_3}{|}}{\underset{\underset{O}{\|}}{C}}-C-\overset{}{N}-CH_2-C-N-C-C-$$

   (a) Draw the structure of the part of the molecule known as the peptide link.
   (b) (i) How many different amino acids would be produced in the breakdown of this part of the polymer?
      (ii) Draw a structural formula for each of these amino acids.
      (iii) What type of reaction would be taking place?

4. The artificial sweetener, aspartame, has the strucure shown.

$$CH_3-O-\overset{}{\underset{\underset{O}{\|}}{C}}-CH-NH-\overset{\overset{O}{\|}}{C}-\overset{\overset{NH_2}{|}}{CH}-CH_2-\overset{\overset{O}{\|}}{C}-O-CH_3$$

Aspartame's sweetness depends on the shape and structure of the molecule. **Two** amino acids, aspartic acid and phenylalanine, are formed when it is hydrolysed.

   (a) Draw a structural formula for each of the amino acids produced during hydrolysis.
   (b) Suggest a reason why aspartame is **not** used in food that will be cooked, but can be used in cold drinks.

Exercise 2.15   **Fats and oils**

1. (a) Give **one** reason why fats and oils can be a useful part of a balanced diet.
    (b) Explain why oils tend to have lower melting points than fats.

2. The structure of an oil can be represented as shown.

    (a) Draw the structure of the fat which could be produced by "hardening" this oil.
    (b) What is the effect of hardening on the melting point of this oil?
    (c) Name the type of chemical reaction which takes place during the hardening process.

3. The hydrolysis of fats produces fatty acids and glycerol.
    (a) Draw a structural formula for glycerol.
    (b) State the ratio of glycerol molecules to fatty acid molecules.

4. A triglyceride produces only glycerol and palmitic acid, on hydrolysis.

    $$CH_3(CH_2)_{14}-\overset{\overset{\displaystyle O}{\|}}{C}-OH$$

    palmitic acid

    (a) To which set of compounds do triglycerides belong?
    (b) Draw a structural formula for the triglyceride.
    (c) Explain whether the triglyceride is likely to be a fat or an oil.

5. Mutton fat contains a compound called tristearin.
    Tristearin is broken down in the body during digestion.
    (a) Name the type of chemical reaction which takes place.
    (b) The break down of tristearin produces a fatty acid.
        (i) Is the fatty acid saturated or unsaturated?
        (ii) Name the other product of this reaction.

    $$H-\overset{\overset{\displaystyle H}{|}}{\underset{\underset{\displaystyle H}{|}}{C}}-O-\overset{\overset{\displaystyle O}{\|}}{C}-C_{17}H_{35}$$

    tristearin

Unit 3

Exercise 3.1 Acids and alkalis

1. (a) What is meant by the pH of a solution?
    (b) Describe how the pH of a solution can be measured.
    (c) What colours do acids turn pH paper?
    (d) What range of pH values can be shown by acids?
    (e) What colours do alkalis turn pH paper?
    (f) What range of pH values can be shown by alkalis?
    (g) What colour do neutral solutions turn pH paper?
    (h) What is the pH of neutral solutions?

2. (a) (i) Name **three** laboratory acids.
        (ii) Name **three** house-hold solutions which are acidic.
    (b) (i) Name **three** laboratory alkalis.
        (ii) Name **three** house-hold solutions which are alkalis.

3. The following is a report given by the Wellcare Company to a fish farmer.

WELLCARE REPORT
Water test
This showed the water was pH 5.
Action needed
The water should be treated to increase the pH

    (a) Describe how you would use Universal indicator or pH paper to measure the pH of the water.
    (b) Suggest a cause for the low pH.
    (c) Give the chemical name of a substance which could be used to increase the pH of the water.

4. A gardener tests the pH of the soil in his garden. The soil has a pH of 5.8.
    The table shows the pH range in which different vegetables will grow successfully.

Vegetable	pH range
broad beans	5.5 - 7.0
carrots	6.0 - 7.5
lettuce	6.5 - 7.5
potatoes	5.5 - 6.5

    (a) Which vegetables will the gardener be able to grow successfully in his garden?
    (b) Name a substance that the gardener could add to the soil in order to grow all of the vegetables successfully.

Intermediate 2 Chemistry

5. Explain why crystals of citric acid have no effect on dry pH paper but turn Universal indicator red.

6. Consider the following list:

    iron(III) oxide,   sodium hydroxide,   carbon dioxide,
    calcium oxide,   nitrogen dioxide,   copper(II) oxide

    (a) Name **two** substances which dissolve to produce a solution which has a pH below 7.

    (b) Name **two** substances which dissolve to produce a solution which has a pH above **7**.

7. Two unknown elements **A** and **B** form oxides. The oxide of **A** gives an aqueous solution of pH 5 while the oxide of **B** gives a solution of pH 10.

    State what this tells us about

    (a) the oxides of **A** and **B**,

    (b) the elements **A** and **B**.

8. Using the apparatus shown, a pupil electrolysed three different acid solutions.

It was noted that a gas was given off at electrode **A** in all cases.
The pupil suspects that the gas is hydrogen.

    (a) What test would show that the gas collected is hydrogen?

    (b) (i) Is **A** the positive or negative electrode?

        (ii) Explain your answer.

9. Some battery acid is spilt on the garage floor. Water is added to the acid, before it is wiped up.

    (a) Which ion is present in solutions of all acids?

    (b) Explain why water is added.

    (c) What happens to the pH of the solution when water is added?

10. (a) What happens to the pH of water when ammonia dissolves in it?

    (b) Chlorine also dissolves in water.

    $$Cl_2(g) + H_2O(l) \rightarrow 2H^+(aq) + OCl^-(aq) + Cl^-(aq)$$

    What happens to the pH of water when it is chlorinated?

11. Kirsty eats three meals a day.
The graph shows how much the pH in her mouth varies during the day.
X, **Y** and **Z** are meal times.

Teeth decay when the pH in the mouth falls below 5.5.

(a) What happens to the pH in the mouth after mealtimes?

(b) Some of Kirsty's friends eat snacks between meals.
Why does this lead to more tooth decay?

(c) Suggest why many toothpastes are alkaline.

12. Chromium(VI) oxide reacts with water to form chromic acid.

$$CrO_3(s) \quad + \quad H_2O(l) \quad \rightarrow \quad H_2CrO_4(aq)$$

Suggest what is unusual about the reaction between chromium(VI) oxide and water.

13. White phosphorus readily catches fire in air.
The following diagrams show this reaction.

(a) Why does the reaction produce an acidic solution?

(b) (i) What would have been the effect on the final water level inside the tube, if a larger piece of phosphorus had been used?

(ii) Explain your answer.

14. Pure water is added to a solution with a pH of 12.
    (a) Which two ions are present in pure water?
    (b) Which contains more hydroxide ions, the solution or the pure water?
    (c) What happens to the concentration of hydroxide ions in the solution as the water is added ?

15. Acid solutions contain $H^+(aq)$ ions; so does pure water.
    (a) Explain why pure water is not an acid.
    (b) When water is added to an acid solution the pH rises.
        (i) Explain why this happens.
        (ii) What is the highest value to which the pH can rise?
        (iii) Explain your answer to (ii).

16. A patient who was undergoing heart surgery had the concentration of carbon dioxide in his blood measured continuously.

The pH of his blood was also measured

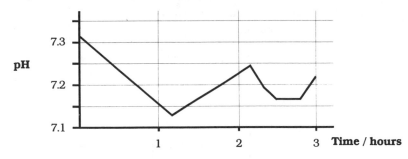

    (a) What happens to the acidity of his blood during the first hour.
    (b) How does the change in concentration of carbon dioxide in his blood affect the pH?
    (c) Carbon dioxide reacts with water.
$$CO_2(g) \; + \; H_2O(l) \; \rightleftharpoons \; H^+(aq) \; + \; HCO_3^-(aq)$$
    How does the equation explain the effect of an increase in concentration of carbon dioxide on the pH of blood?

17. As a homework exercise, pupils were asked to find the pH values of a number of substances found in the home.

One pupil wrote down her results as follows.

bicarbonate of soda - 9; vinegar - 4; drain cleaner - 14; cola drink - 3; milk - 8; indigestion pill - 10; window cleaner - 12; washing-up liquid - 7; lemon juice- 3.

Present the results of the home exercise in **two** different ways.

18. This graph shows how much lime a gardener needs to add to produce a soil of the desired pH, e.g. if the soil had a pH of 4, but a pH of 7 was required, 1.3 kg of lime would be needed for every 10 m^2 of soil.

Find the mass of lime which is needed to increase the pH of soi

(a) from pH 6 to pH 7 in a 10 m^2 garden,

(b) from pH 7 to pH 8 in a 10 m^2 garden,

(c) from pH 6 to pH 8 in a 100 m^2 garden.

19. Ethanoic acid, found in vinegar, is the second member of a family of acids which all contain carbon. Information about five of the acids is shown.

Acid	Boiling point / °C
A	164
B	141
C	118
D	186
E	102

(a) State the number of carbon atoms present in a molecule of **C**.

(b) Estimate the boiling point of the acid with 6 carbon atoms per molecule.

Intermediate 2 Chemistry

20. Sodium hypochlorite is a substance present in household bleaches. It gives them their bleaching action.

The concentration of sodium hypochlorite in a bleach can be found by adding an excess of dilute hydrochloric acid to a measured sample of the bleach. The acid reacts with the sodium hypochlorite and the volume of chlorine given off is measured.

$$NaOCl(aq) \ + \ 2HCl(aq) \ \rightarrow \ NaCl(aq) \ + \ H_2O(l) \ + \ Cl_2(g)$$

In an investigation of three different household bleaches, the following results were obtained.

Bleach	Volume of bleach used /cm^3	Volume of chlorine produced /cm^3
A	6	100
B	9	150
C	4	90

(a) Find, **by calculation**, which bleach contains most sodium hypochlorite per litre.

(b) Some cleaners contain acid.
Why should such cleaners not be used with bleach?

Exercise 3.2   Concentration

1. Calculate the number of moles of potassium hydroxide which must be dissolved to make each of the following solutions.
    (a)   500 cm^3 of 1 mol l^{-1}
    (b)   200 cm^3 of 0.5 mol l^{-1}
    (c)   100 cm^3 of 0.1 mol l^{-1}
    (d)   2 litres of 0.25 mol l^{-1}
    (e)   250 cm^3 of 2 mol l^{-1}

2. Calculate the concentration of each of the following solutions of hydrochloric acid.
    (a)   1 mol of hydrogen chloride dissolved to make 100 cm^3 of solution
    (b)   2 mol of hydrogen chloride dissolved to make 1 litre of solution
    (c)   0.1 mol of hydrogen chloride dissolved to make 500 cm^3 of solution
    (d)   0.5 mol of hydrogen chloride dissolved to make 250 cm^3 of solution
    (e)   0.4 mol of hydrogen chloride dissolved to make 200 cm^3 of solution

3. Calculate the volume of each of the following solutions of sodium hydroxide.
    (a)   1 mol l^{-1} solution containing 2 mol of solute
    (b)   0.5 mol l^{-1} solution containing 1 mol of solute
    (c)   2 mol l^{-1} solution containing 0.1 mol of solute
    (d)   0.1 mol l^{-1} solution containing 0.5 mol of solute
    (e)   0.4 mol l^{-1} solution containing 0.1 mol of solute.

4. Calculate the number of grams of substance required to make each of the following solutions.
    (a)   50 cm^3 of NaOH(aq), concentration 2 mol l^{-1}
    (b)   100 cm^3 of KOH(aq), concentration 0.5 mol l^{-1}
    (c)   1 litre of Na$_2$CO$_3$(aq), concentration 0.1 mol l^{-1}
    (d)   25 cm^3 of lithium nitrate solution, concentration 0.2 mol l^{-1}
    (e)   250 cm^3 of ammonium sulphate solution, concentration 1 mol l^{-1}
    (f)   200 cm^3 of calcium nitrate solution, concentration 0.25 mol l^{-1}

5. Calculate the concentration of each of the following solutions.
    (a)   5.65 g of NaCl dissolved to make 1 litre of solution
    (b)   2.5 g of CaCO$_3$ dissolved to make 100 cm^3 of solution
    (c)   8 g of NaOH dissolved to make 250 cm^3 of solution
    (d)   2.02 g of potassium nitrate dissolved to make 50 cm^3 of solution
    (e)   4 g of copper(II) sulphate dissolved to make 100 cm^3 of solution
    (f)   1.27 g of iron(II) chloride dissolved to make 2 litres of solution

Exercise 3.3   Strong and weak acids and bases

1. The terms weak and strong and dilute and concentrated are often confused.
    (a) Explain clearly the difference between
        (i)   a dilute acid and a concentrated acid,
        (ii) a weak acid and a strong acid.
    (b) Give **one** example of
        (i)   a weak acid,
        (ii) a strong acid.
    (c) As a strong acid is diluted, state what happens to
        (i)   the concentration of hydrogen ions,
        (ii) the number of hydrogen ions.

2. Consider the following list of acids:

    ethanoic acid,   hydrochloric acid,   nitric acid,   sulphuric acid

    Arrange the acids into two columns, headed strong acids and weak acids.

3. Acid **X** is a strong acid; acid **Y** is a weak acid. Both have the same concentration.
    (a) Which has the higher conductivity?
    (b) Which reacts faster with magnesium?
    (c) 25 cm^3 of 2 mol l^{-1} sodium hydroxide solution is required to neutralise a fixed volume of acid **X**.
        (i)   What volume of the same alkali would be required to neutralise the same volume of acid **Y**?
        (ii) Explain your answer.

4.

Acid	pH of 2 mol l^{-1} solution
A CCl$_3$COOH	0.50
B CHCl$_2$COOH	0.90

(a) Which is the stronger acid?
(b) Explain your answer.

5. A pupil carried out three experiments to compare the properties of sodium hydroxide solution with ammonia solution.

Experiment	Sodium hydroxide solution	Ammonia solution
pH	higher	lower
Conductivity	higher	lower
Volume of dilute acid required to neutralise 25 cm^3 of alkali	same	same

(a) Write an equation to show why ammonia is a weak base.

(b) Explain why the concentrations of the two alkalis must be kept the same in each of the experiments.

(c) Explain the results of each experiment.

Exercise 3.4   Reactions of acids

1. (a) Explain what is meant by a neutralisation reaction.
   (b) What happens to the pH of an acid as it is neutralised?
   (c) What happens to the pH of an alkali as it is neutralised?
   (d) Write an equation to show the ions involved in **any** acid / **any** alkali reaction.

2. (a) Explain why gardeners add lime to soil which is acidic.
   (b) Explain why Milk of Magnesia is taken to relieve acid indigestion.

3. In certain hard-water areas, scale can build up on the inside of kettles.
   When tested with Universal indicator, the scale shows a pH above 7.
   (a) Explain why vinegar could be used to descale kettles.
   (b) Name the kind of reaction that would occur.
   (c) Name **one** of the products of the reaction.

4. During manned flights in space rockets, carbon dioxide builds up in the air inside the cabin.
   Explain why the rockets also carry a supply of lithium hydroxide.

5. (a) (i) Which gas is produced when a metal carbonate reacts with a dilute acid?
       (ii) Describe the test for this gas.
   (b) Name the products of each of the following reactions.
       (i) calcium carbonate and dilute sulphuric acid
       (ii) sodium carbonate and dilute nitric acid
   (c) Write an equation to show the ions involved in **any** acid / **any** metal carbonate reaction.

6. (a) (i) Which gas is produced when a metal reacts with dilute hydrochloric acid?
       (ii) Describe the test for this gas.
   (b) Name the products of each of the following reactions.
       (i) calcium and dilute hydrochloric acid
       (ii) magnesium and dilute sulphuric acid
   (c) Write an equation to show the formation of this gas in **any** acid / **any** metal reaction.

7. Crystals of magnesium sulphate can be made by adding excess magnesium oxide to dilute sulphuric acid.
   (a) Name the kind of reaction which takes place.
   (b) What happens to the pH of the dilute acid?
   (c) Describe how the excess magnesium oxide can be removed from the solution.

8. An experiment was carried out on a substance **X**.

dilute hydrochloric acid
+
substance X

lime water
turns cloudy

    (a) Which gas turns lime water cloudy?

    (b) From this experiment, what can be learned about **X**?

9. Sodium nitrate and sodium carbonate are both white solids. Given a sample of each, describe a test you could carry out to discover which was which.

    (Give the results of the test.)

10. John spilled sulphuric acid from a car battery on his garage floor. First he poured water over the acid. Then he sprinkled washing soda (sodium carbonate) on it before mopping it up.

    (a) Why did John add water to the acid?

    (b) (i) Name the type of reaction which takes place when washing soda is added to sulphuric acid.

       (ii) Name the gas produced in the reaction.

11. Many pollution problems are linked to the release of sulphur dioxide into the air.

    (a) Give **one** source of sulphur dioxide in air.

    (b) What name is given to a solution of sulphur dioxide in rain-water?

    (c) Give **three** examples of the damage which can be caused by this solution.

    (d) (i) Name **one** other gas which causes similar pollution problems.

       (ii) Give **one** source of this gas.

12. Tom had indigestion caused by too much hydrochloric acid in his stomach. To make himself feel better, he took a Calmo indigestion tablet. The active ingredient in the tablet is a metal hydroxide.

    (a) (i) Name one of the products which is formed when the active ingredient reacts with hydrochloric acid.

       (ii) Name the type of reaction which occurs.

    (c) Describe an experiment which could be carried out to show that a Calmo tablet is effective in neutralising acid.

13. Two chemical factories were built close to different rivers. The soap works polluted the West River with sodium hydroxide. The explosives factory polluted the North River with nitric acid.

Government inspectors took water samples from the points **A, B, C, D** and **E**. They tested each sample with pH indicator solution.

(a) Which **two** water samples should be compared to show that the soap works was causing pollution.

(b) The water sample from point **E** was found to be neutral, despite the pollution.

Give a reason for this result.

14. Carbon monoxide can be prepared, in a fume cupboard, by passing carbon dioxide over heated carbon.

(a) Explain why potassium hydroxide solution removes unreacted carbon dioxide.

(b) Draw a suitable arrangement for collecting the carbon monoxide gas.

15. John was given the task of separating copper metal from a mixture containing copper(II) oxide and copper metal. The diagram shows what he did.

Describe in detail how John separated the copper metal from the mixture.

16. Consider the substances listed below.

    (i)   sodium hydroxide   (ii)   copper(II) oxide   (iii) sodium chloride
    (iv)   potassium sulphate   (v)   magnesium   (vi)   sodium oxide
    (vii) carbon   (viii) lithium nitrate   (ix)   iron(III) hydroxide
    (x)   barium oxide   (xi)   zinc   (xii) calcium sulphate

    (a)   Which substances can be classified as bases?
    (b)   Which substances dissolve in water to form alkalis?

17. Chlorine can be prepared in the laboratory by the reaction of concentrated hydrochloric acid with manganese(IV) oxide.

    Using **all** the equipment given below, draw a labelled diagram to show how chlorine gas can be produced and collected.

concentrated   manganese(IV)   rubber   test
hydrochloric acid   oxide   connector   tube

separating funnel   beaker of   delivery   side arm
and rubber stopper   water   tube   conical flask

18.

Workcard 1

Testing carbon dioxide

(G)

Apparatus and chemicals

clamp stand

delivery tube

test tubes

Universal indicator

chalk

Do this

1. Put some powdered chalk in a test tube.
2. Clamp the test tube in the clamp stand.
3. Fit the delivery tube to the test tube.
4. Put 10 cm³ of water into the second test tube and add a few drops of Universal indicator.
5. Place the end of the delivery tube into the indicator.
6. Heat the chalk with the bunsen burner.

(a) Copy and complete the diagram of the apparatus for the experiment.
Label your diagram to show the chemicals and where you would heat.

(b) What colour would the Universal indicator turn?

19. Calum added 2.0 cm^3 of sodium hydroxide solution to 25.0 cm^3 of hydrochloric acid. He noted the temperature rise.

stirring thermometer

25.0 cm^3 of hydrochloric acid and 2.0 cm^3 of sodium hydroxide solution.

insulated beaker

He then repeated his experiment using different volumes of the sodium hydroxide solution. Calum's results are shown in the table.

Temperature rise / °C	Volume of added sodium hydroxide solution / cm^3
1.6	2.0
3.7	4.0
6.0	6.0
8.4	8.0
10.2	10.0
11.9	12.0
11.8	14.0
11.0	16.0
9.6	18.0

(a) Explain why the temperature rises in each of the experiments.

(b) Draw a **line graph** of his results

(c) What volume of sodium hydroxide solution was needed to neutralise the hydrochloric acid?
You may wish to refer to your graph.

(d) Calum carried out a second set of experiments using more concentrated sodium hydroxide solution.

How would the volume of sodium hydroxide solution needed to neutralise the acid have compared with your answer to part (c)?

Exercise 3.5   Volumetric titrations

1. (a) What volume of hydrochloric acid (concentration 0.1 mol l^{-1}) is required to neutralise 50 cm^3 of sodium hydroxide solution (concentration 0.2 mol l^{-1})?

    (b) What is the concentration of sulphuric acid if 50 cm^3 are neutralised by 25 cm^3 of potassium hydroxide solution (concentration 1 mol l^{-1})?

    (c) What volume of nitric acid (concentration 2 mol l^{-1}) is required to neutralise 20 cm^3 of sodium hydroxide solution (concentration 0.5 mol l^{-1})?

    (d) What is the concentration of hydrochloric acid if 12.6 cm^3 neutralises 20 cm^3 of potassium hydroxide solution(concentration 0.1 mol l^{-1})?

    (e) What is the concentration of sulphuric acid if 17.3 cm^3 neutralises 25 cm^3 of sodium hydroxide solution (concentration 0.5 mol l^{-1})?

2. Car batteries contain sulphuric acid. The concentration of the acid is to be checked by carrying out a titration. For safety reasons, the battery acid has been diluted to exactly one hundredth of its original concentration.

    The grid below contains a number of steps which could be used in the titration.

A add universal indicator solution to the flask	B evaporate to dryness	C measure 10 cm^3 of acid into the flask
D fill burette with acid	E repeat using smaller additions near the end point, to get a more accurate result	F note volume required for neutralisation
G measure 20 cm^3 of alkali into the flask	H run in acid 1cm^3 at a time shaking the flask after each addititon	I repeat, using same volumes of acid and alkali, but with no indicator

    Write down **in the correct order** the letters for the steps which should be used.

3. Hard water forms a scum with soap. This hardness can be caused by dissolved calcium ions.

    Klenzmore is a soap company which tests hardness of different water samples.

    The samples are titrated with an acid called EDTA, using a suitable indicator.

    One mole of calcium ions reacts with **one** mole of EDTA.

    In one titration 18.6 cm^3 of 0.12 mol l^{-1} EDTA reacted with 25.0 cm^3 of a water sample.

    Calculate the concentration of calcium ions, in mol l^{-1}, in the sample.

4. Iain determined the mass of iron present in a piece of wire.

Step 1. He completely reacted the wire with dilute sulphuric acid.
This produced a solution of iron(II) sulphate, $FeSO_4$.

Step 2. He found the volume of potassium permanganate solution needed to
react with the iron(II) sulphate solution by titration.

(a) Why was the wire reacted with sulphuric acid in Step 1?

(b) Name the gas formed in Step 1.

(c) Iain found that 20.2 cm^3 of potassium permanganate solution,
concentration 0.15 mol l^{-1}, were needed to react with the iron(II) sulphate
solution.

  (i) How many moles of potassium permanganate were needed to react
with the iron(II) sulphate solution.

  (ii) **One** mole of potassium permanganate reacts with **five** moles of iron(II)
sulphate.

  Calculate the mass of iron present in the steel wire.

5. Stuart wanted to prepare ammonium sulphate.

He added 0.5 mol l^{-1} sulphuric acid from a burette to 20 cm^3 of 0.5 mol l^{-1}
ammonia solution in a conical flask with pH indicator.

The equation for the reaction is:

$$2NH_3(aq) \ + H_2SO_4(aq) \quad \rightarrow \quad (NH_4)_2SO_4(aq)$$

(a) Calculate the volume of sulphuric acid Stuart used to neutralise the
ammonia solution.

(b) The indicator was remove from the ammonium sulphate solution by
filtering the solution through charcoal.

How would Stuart then obtain a sample of solid ammonium sulphate from
the solution?

Exercise 3.6

Salts

1. Consider the substances listed below.

   (i)   sodium hydroxide (ii)   copper(II) oxide (iii) sodium chloride
   (iv) potassium sulphate (v)   magnesium (vi) sodium oxide
   (vii) carbon (viii) lithium nitrate (ix) iron(III) hydroxide
   (x)   barium oxide (xi) zinc (xii) calcium sulphate

   Which substances can be classified as salts?

2. Name the products which would be formed in the reaction between each of the following solutions.

   (a) potassium hydroxide and nitric acid
   (b) sodium hydroxide and sulphuric acid
   (c) lithium hydroxide and hydrochloric acid

3. Name the acid and the alkali which could be used to prepare solutions of each of the following compounds.

   (a) sodium chloride
   (b) potassium sulphate
   (c) barium nitrate

4. Name the products of each of the following reactions.

   (a) magnesium carbonate and dilute sulphuric acid
   (b) potassium carbonate and dilute nitric acid

5. Name the products of each of the following reactions.

   (a) aluminium and dilute hydrochloric acid
   (b) zinc and dilute sulphuric acid

6.

potassium hydroxide solution → **neutraliser** → **potassium chloride solution**

reagent X →

   (a) Name reagent **X**.
   (b) Describe how to produce a dry sample of potassium chloride from the solution.

7.

| hydrochloric acid | + | solution **A** | → | sodium chloride solution |

    +

| magnesium |

    ↓

| solution **X** |

    +

| gas **Y** |

(a) State the name of each of the following.

    (i) solution **A**   (ii) solution **X**   (iii) gas **Y**

(b) State the type of reaction that occurs when hydrochloric acid reacts with solution **A**.

8. During a practical exercise, Yasmin recorded the following notes in her laboratory notebook. She was preparing crystals of blue copper(II) sulphate.

1. I added the black oxide to the acid until no more dissolved.

black oxide

acid solution

2. I then filtered the solution to remove any unreacted oxide.

unreacted oxide

filtrate

3. The filtrate was left to evaporate for 3 days.

blue crystals

(a) Name the black oxide and the acid solution.

(b) Name the type of chemical reaction that took place in the beaker.

(c) Name the ion which is coloured blue.

9. Chromic acid, H_2CrO_4(aq), forms a salt with potassium hydroxide.
   (a) How many moles of potassium hydroxide would be needed to neutralise completely one mole of chromic acid.
   (b) Name the salt formed in the reaction.
      (You may wish to use page 6 of the data booklet to help you.)

10. Jack prepared copper(II) sulphate by adding excess solid copper(II) oxide to sulphuric acid.

    Jill prepared sodium chloride by the addition of sodium hydroxide solution to hydrochloric acid.

    Explain why Jack and Jill used different methods to prepare their salts.

11. For each of the following reactions, rewrite the equations as ionic equations, omitting spectator ions.
    (a) $NaOH(aq) + HCl(aq) \rightarrow NaCl(aq) + H_2O(l)$
    (b) $2KOH(aq) + H_2SO_4(aq) \rightarrow K_2SO_4(aq) + 2H_2O(l)$
    (c) $K_2CO_3(aq) + 2HCl(aq) \rightarrow 2KCl(aq) + H_2O(l) + CO_2(g)$

12. The graph shows how the level of nitrates in the soil of a farmer's field varied throughout a particular year.

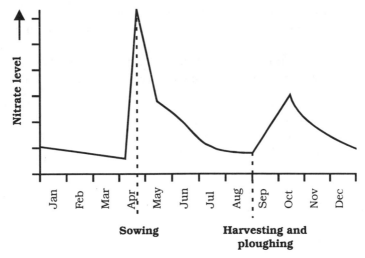

    (a) Suggest why the level of nitrates increased in April.
    (b) Suggest why the level of nitrates decreased from April to August.
    (c) During periods of heavy rain, nitrates from the soil are washed into rivers. What effect does this have on the rivers?

13. Ammonium nitrate fertiliser can be made by the NITRAM Process as shown.

   (a) Write the formula for ammonia and ammonium nitrate.
   (b) Name **X**.

14. Nitrate fertilisers are made from nitric acid.

   (a) Name reagent **A**.
   (b) Name the other product of this reaction.
   (c) Name the kind of reaction which is taking place.
   (d) State **two** reasons why nitrate compounds are useful fertilisers.

15. (a) Why do farmers add lime (calcium oxide) to their fields?
    (b) Explain why ammonium sulphate fertiliser should not be added at the same time.

16. Lawn sand contains ammonium sulphate and iron(II) sulphate. One compound improves grass growth, the other is present to kill moss.

   (a) Name the ion which is present in lawn sand to kill moss.
   (b) Ammonium sulphate is made from ammonia.
   Name the chemical which reacts with ammonia to form ammonium sulphate.

17. Heating a mixture of solid ammonium sulphate and sodium hydroxide pellets produces ammonia gas. Ammonia reacts with iron oxide.

   Draw a diagram to show apparatus you would set up to make ammonia gas and to pass it over hot iron oxide.

   In your diagram label the apparatus and chemicals used.

18. The graph shows the masses of three elements used to make synthetic fertilisers between 1900 and 1990.

(a) In which year were equal masses of nitrogen and phosphorus fertilisers made?

(b) What trend is shown by the graph for the use of all three elements between 1940 and 1990?

(c) Name a synthetic fertiliser containing potassium and nitrogen as well as oxygen.

(d) Calcium phosphate is readily available but cannot be used directly in fertilisers.

Suggest why it is unsuitable.

You may wish to use the data booklet.

19. A chemistry class was studying the movement of molecules in gases.

The experiment shown was set up.

The cover slips were removed.
After a time, a white solid, ammonium chloride, formed.

(a) Explain why the white solid appeared.

(b) What does the position of the white solid indicate about the movement of ammonia gas compared to hydrogen chloride gas?

Exercise 3.7   Precipitation

1. An insoluble product can be formed in the reaction between solutions.
    (a) Name this type of reaction.
    (b) Identify the insoluble product in each of the following reactions.
        (i) potassium sulphate solution and barium chloride solution
        (ii) calcium nitrate solution and sodium sulphate solution
        (iii) sodium chloride solution and silver nitrate solution

2. (a) Magnesium carbonate has a solubility of less than 1g l⁻¹.
        (i) From the following list of substances select **two** which together could
             be used to make magnesium carbonate:

             magnesium, magnesium nitrate, barium carbonate,
                  carbon, magnesium oxide, sodium carbonate
        (ii) Describe in detail how you would use these two substances to prepare
              a dry sample of magnesium carbonate.

3. Sodium sulphate solution and
    barium chloride solution were **sodium sulphate**   **barium chloride**
    mixed as shown.   **solution**   **solution**

    colourless solution

    white solid

    (a) Name the white solid.
    (b) Name the type of reaction which occurred.
    (c) Name the technique which could be used to remove the white solid from the
         solution.

4. Karen made a solution of table salt
    (sodium chloride solution). When she   **sodium chloride**
    added a few drops of the salt solution   **solution**
    to silver nitrate solution, a solid
    formed at the bottom of the beaker.
    (a) What is the name of the solid?   **silver nitrate**
                                                                solution
    (b) She then added a few drops of
         the solution to potassium nitrate
         solution.   **solid formed**

         Why did **no** solid form at the
         bottom of the beaker.

5. Patients with stomach problems are given a "barium meal" before being X-rayed. It consists of a suspension of barium sulphate in water.
    This salt can be prepared in the laboratory by a precipitation reaction.

    (a) Name **two** salt solutions which could be mixed to prepare barium sulphate.

    (b) The barium sulphate is separated from the reaction mixture by filtration. If the barium sulphate solution was not washed before it was dried, it would be contaminated.

    Name **two** compounds which could possibly contaminate the barium sulphate sample.

    (c) Barium compounds are toxic.

    Suggest why people can drink "barium meals" without suffering any ill effects.

6. For each of the following reactions, rewrite the equations as ionic equations, omitting spectator ions.

    (a) $AgNO_3(aq) + NaCl(aq) \rightarrow NaNO_3(aq) + AgCl(s)$

    (b) $CuSO_4(aq) + 2NaOH(aq) \rightarrow Na_2SO_4(aq) + Cu(OH)_2(s)$

    (c) $BaCl_2(aq) + Na_2SO_4(aq) \rightarrow 2NaCl(aq) + BaSO_4(s)$

    (d) $CuCl_2(aq) + Na_2CO_3(aq) \rightarrow 2NaCl(aq) + CuCO_3(s)$

7. Sodium hydroxide solution often contains dissolved sodium carbonate as an impurity. This is caused by some of the sodium hydroxide reacting with carbon dioxide from the air.
    The carbonate ions can be removed by adding a few drops of barium chloride solution. The equation for the reaction is:

    $BaCl_2(aq) + Na_2CO_3(aq) \rightarrow BaCO_3(s) + 2NaCl(aq)$

    (a) Name an ion which will be an impurity in the final sodium hydroxide solution.

    (b) Rewrite the equation as an ionic equation omitting spectator ions.

8. Common salt is extracted from salt mines by pumping in water to dissolve it. The salt solution which is obtained contains magnesium sulphate as an impurity.
    The magnesium ions are removed by adding sodium hydroxide solution.

    $Mg^{2+}(aq) + SO_4^{2-}(aq) + 2Na^+(aq) + 2OH^-(aq)$
    $\rightarrow Mg^{2+}(OH^-)_2(s) + 2Na^+(aq) + SO_4^{2-}(aq)$

    (a) (i) Name the type of reaction taking place between the magnesium sulphate solution and the sodium hydroxide solution.

    (ii) Name the spectator ions in the reaction.

    (b) The products of the reaction can be separated by filtration.

    Draw and label the apparatus you would use in the laboratory to carry out this process.

Exercise 3.8   The electrochemical series

1. A simple cell can be made up using a lemon and two different metals.

(a) The lemon juice is an electrolyte.

What is the purpose of an electrolyte in a cell?

(b) Clearly state the direction of the electron flow through the wire.

(c) What would happen to the reading on the voltmeter if the iron was replaced with a piece of zinc?

2. When magnesium ribbon is added to copper sulphate solution, the ribbon starts to break up at the surface, a brown solid forms, and the solution eventually becomes colourless.

Magnesium ribbon does not react with sodium sulphate solution.

Explain these observations.

3. A simple dry cell can be made from everyday materials.

The paste is made from salt (sodium chloride), water and porridge. Porridge is composed mainly of starch.

(a) Clearly state the direction in which electrons flow through the wire.

(b) Why could calcium carbonate **not** be used as an electrolyte?

(c) Would the voltage be higher or lower if an aluminium can were used?

. The arrangement shown below is
used to produce a flow of electrons.

(a) In which direction do
the electrons flow through
the meter?

(b) Explain your answer.

. (a) Using magnesium, copper,
magnesium sulphate solution and
copper sulphate solution, state what
A, **B**, **C** and **D** must be to give a flow
of electrons in the direction shown

(b) (i) What is **E** on the diagram known as?
(ii) Why is it necessary?
(iii) Why is sodium chloride solution suitable but sugar solution is **not**?

. The diagram represents a cell giving a reading of 1.1 volts.

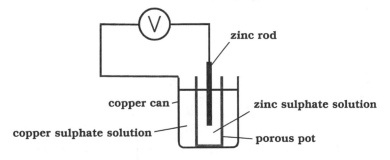

(a) State the direction of electron flow through the meter.
(b) What difference would there be in the meter reading if the zinc was replaced
by magnesium and the zinc sulphate solution by magnesium sulphate
solution?
(c) If the cell shown was allowed to run for 24 hours, what visible signs of a
chemical change would there be?

7. James put a copper coin into silver nitrate solution. The coin turned a grey colour.

   He the put the coin into sodium chloride solution. The coin did not change in any way.

   Explain what was observed in each case.

8. The Italian professor, Alessandro Volta, made one of the first batteries. It was called a "Voltaic pile". The following diagram shows the pile connected to a meter for measuring current.

   (a) When the sodium chloride solution is replaced by potassium nitrate solution, a reading is still obtained on the meter. When ethanol is used, no reading is obtained.

   Explain each of these results.

   (b) What will happen to the reading on the meter if the zinc is replaced by tin?

9.

   Three metals were tested in the experiment above.
   The results are shown in the table.

Metal tested	Voltage / V	Direction of electron flow
R	0.3	zinc to metal R
S	0.4	metal S to zinc
T	1.0	zinc to metal T

   (a) State which **one** of the four metals (**R, S, T** and zinc) is highest in the electrochemical series.

   (b) Arrange the four metals in order of their position in the electrochemical series, with the highest first.

10. Refer to the diagram.

(a) (i) In which direction do the electrons flow through the meter?

(ii) Explain your answer.

(b) Name a metal which could replace magnesium and produce a flow of electrons in the opposite direction through the meter.

(c) What would happen to the meter reading if the copper rod was replaced by an iron rod?

(d) (i) What would happen to the meter reading if the sodium chloride solution was replaced by sugar solution?

(ii) Explain your answer.

11. Bill wanted to show that chemicals can be used to produce an electric current.

When the crocodile clips were attached to certain parts of the apparatus, the bulb lit.

(a) State clearly where the crocodile clips should have been attached.

(b) In a second experiment, the cardboard container was replaced by a glass beaker.

Explain why the bulb did not light.

12. Using the apparatus below, the following results were obtained.

filter paper soaked in sodium chloride solution

test metal

copper block

Test metal	Voltmeter reading / V
lithium	2.9
sodium	2.4
magnesium	1.6
iron	0.5
tin	0.4
copper	0.0
silver	-0.4

(a) What name is given to this kind of series of metals arranged from voltmeter readings?

(b) Explain why magnesium ribbon does **not** react with sodium sulphate solution

(d) Suppose the copper block was replaced by a block of tin.
   (i) What would be the reading on the voltmeter if the test metal is iron?
   (ii) What would be the reading on the voltmeter if the test metal is silver?
   (iii) Which metal could be used as the test metal to give a voltmeter reading of approximately 1.2 V?

13. Part of the electrochemical series is shown opposite.

From its position in the series, state what would happen when metal **X** is added to an aqueous solution of

(a) copper(II) sulphate,
(b) magnesium chloride.

magnesium
metal **X**
iron
tin
copper

14. The cells which power heart pacemakers contain lithium metal.

negative electrode

stainless steel casing

lithium metal

insulating material

electrolyte layer

positive electrode

(a) Explain why lithium metal is a good choice for the negative electrode.
(b) What is the purpose of the electrolyte layer in the cell?
(c) Suggest why water is **not** used in the electrolyte layer.

15. Nicola was given a chemistry set as a birthday present. One of the activities was to use electricity from a chemical reaction to operate a digital stop clock. Nicola was able to make the stop clock work using only the items shown in the diagram.

(a) Draw a labelled diagram to show how Nicola arranged the items to make the experiment work.

(b) Nicola stirred the copper sulphate solution with an iron screwdriver.

   (i) What colour would Nicola have seen on the blade of the screwdriver?

   (ii) What caused this to take place?

(c) Nicola repeated the stirring of the copper sulphate solution with a piece of aluminium.

   Suggest why there was **not** a reaction in this case.

Exercise 3.9   Redox reactions

1. (a) State whether or not a reaction takes place when each of the following metals is added to the solution.

    (i)   magnesium added to copper(II) sulphate solution

    (ii) copper added to sodium chloride solution

    (iii) zinc added to silver nitrate solution

    (iv) copper added to zinc sulphate solution

    (v)   silver added to copper(II) chloride solution

    (vi) aluminium added to magnesium nitrate solution

    (b) Write ion-electron equations for the reactions which occur.

2. A pupil carried out a series of experiments involving the displacement of one metal by another. Four different metals were used and two of them, **P** and **Q** were from unlabelled bottles. Each metal was placed, in turn, in various metal salt solutions.

    The following table shows the results of the experiments. A tick (√) indicates that a displacement reaction was seen to occur; a cross (×) that no reaction occurred.

	Solutions			
Metal	zinc sulphate	lead nitrate	copper(II) chloride	silver nitrate
magnesium	√	√	√	√
copper	×	×	×	√
P	×	√	√	√
Q	√	√	√	√

    (a) Suggest names for metals **P** and **Q** which would give the results shown in the table.

    (b) (i)   What would have been the colour of the solution after the copper had reacted with the silver nitrate solution?

         (ii) For this reaction, write the ion-electron equation to show how the copper would have changed.

3. A piece of zinc is added to copper(II) chloride solution.

    (a) State what happens

         (i)   to the piece of zinc,

         (ii) to the copper(II) ions,

         (iii) to the colour of the solution.

    (b) Write ion-electron equations for the oxidation and reduction reactions which occur.

4.

Oxidation takes place at the magnesium electrode.

(a)   In which direction will electrons flow through the meter?

(b)   Write the ion-electron equation for the reaction at the magnesium electrode.

(c)   Which electrode will decrease in mass?

(d)   Write the ion-electron equation for the reaction at electrode **X**.

5.

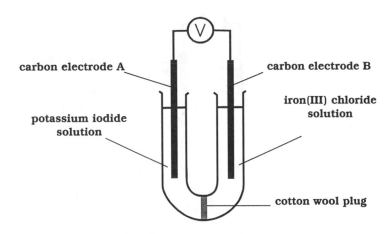

The reaction occuring at electrode **B** is:

$$Fe^{3+}(aq) \quad + \quad e^- \quad \rightarrow \quad Fe^{2+}(aq)$$

(a)   Name the type of chemical reaction occurring at electrode **B**.

(b)   In which direction do the electrons flow through the meter?

(c)   What product will be formed from iodide ions at electrode **A**?

(d)   Write the ion-electron equation for the reaction at electrode **A**.

6. Some hearing aid batteries contain silver(I) oxide. Silver can be extracted from the silver oxide in spent batteries using a two step process.

    Step1 involves reacting the silver(I) oxide with nitric acid to form silver(I) nitrate solution.

    Step 2 is shown in the following diagram.

    (a)   The reaction in step 2 is an example of a redox reaction.
          Give another name for the type of reaction occurring at this step.
    (b)   Write the ion-electron equation for the reduction reaction.
    (c)   No silver is produced if the metal **X** is platinum.
          What does this indicate about the reactivity of platinum?

7. Electrochemical cells use redox reactions to produce electricity. An example of a cell is shown.

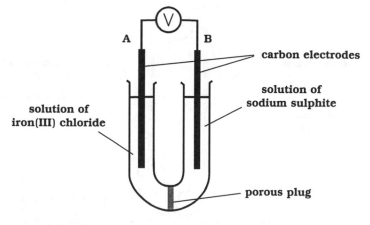

    The reaction taking place at electrode **B** of the above cell is:
    $$SO_3^{2-}(aq) + H_2O(l) \rightarrow SO_4^{2-}(aq) + 2H^+(aq) + 2e^-$$
    (a)   Name the type of reaction taking place at electrode **B**.
    (b)   Clearly state the direction of electron flow through the meter.
    (c)   As the reaction proceeds, iron(III) ions react to form iron(II) ions.
          Explain why this happens.
    (d)   Write the ion-electron equation for the reaction at electrode **A**.

8. Sodium sulphite solution reacts with bromine solution. The sulphite ions are oxidised. The ion-electron equation for the oxidation reaction is:

$$SO_3^{2-}(aq) + H_2O(l) \rightarrow SO_4^{2-}(aq) + 2H^+(aq) + 2e^-$$

This reaction takes place in the cell shown.

(a) On the diagram, identify the two solutions at **X** and **Y** so that the flow of electrons is in the direction shown.

(b) What is the purpose of the filter paper soaked in electrolyte between the beakers?

(c) In the reaction, the bromine solution is reduced.

Write the ion-electron equation for this reaction.

(d) If samples of the two solutions were mixed, what would you see happening?

9. When a compound containing sulphite ions, eg sodium sulphite, is added to bromine water the bromine water is decolourised.

(a) Name the type of reaction which occurs between bromine and sulphite ions.

(b) (i) Write the ion-electron equation to show what happens to the bromine.

   (ii) Write the ion-electron equation to show what happens to the sulphite ions.

10.

sodium sulphite
solution

iron(III) chloride
solution

In the cell shown, the electrons flow through the meter from electrode **A** to electrode **B**.

(a) State the electrode at which

    (i) oxidation takes place,   (ii) reduction takes place.

(b) Write the ion-electron equation for the reaction involving the sulphite ions at electrode **A**.

(c) Explain what happens in the salt bridge.

11. Pure nickel can be obtained by the electrolysis of nickel(II) chloride solution.

(a) Write the ion-electron equation for the formation of the nickel.

(b) Is this an example of oxidation or reduction?

(c) Does this reaction occur at the positive or negative electrode?

12.

chlorine gas out   titanium (+ve electrode)

sodium chloride
solution in →

mercury in →

sodium chloride
solution out

film of mercury (-ve electrode)

→ mercury out

The cell shown is used for the industrial manufacture of chlorine.

(a) In the cell, the sodium chloride is broken up by the electrical energy. What name is given to this process?

(b) Name the kind of reaction which occurs at the mercury electrode.

(c) Write the ion-electron equation for what happens at the titanium electrode.

(d) Suggest an advantage in maintaining a continuous flow of sodium chloride solution.

13. Copper can be purified by electro-refining. This process is illustrated in the diagram.

impure copper

impurities

pure copper

copper chloride solution

The ion-electron equation for the process occurring at the impure electrode is:
$$Cu(s) \rightarrow Cu^{2+}(aq) + 2e^-$$

(a) What name is given to the kind of reaction at the impure electrode?

(b) Is the impure electrode the positive or the negative electrode?

(c) During electro-refining, what happens to the mass of the pure copper electrode?

(d) Write the ion-electron equation for the reaction at the pure copper electrode.

14. Copper(II) chloride solution is electrolysed in the apparatus shown.

Write ion-electron equations for the formation of

(a) the solid,

(b) the gas.

battery

carbon electrodes

solid formed

gas formed

copper(II) chloride solution

15. The following reactions take place at the electrodes when the solution of common salt is electrolysed.

positive electrode: $2Cl^-(aq) \rightarrow Cl_2(g) + 2e^-$

negative electrode: $2H_2O(l) + 2e^- \rightarrow H_2(g) + 2OH^-(aq)$

(a) Name the type of reaction taking place at the negative electrode.

(b) As the electrolysis continues, explain what will happen to the pH of the salt solution.

Exercise 3.10   Metals and metal ores

1. (a) Name **three** metals which are stored under oil.
    (b) What does this indicate about the reactivity of these metals?

2. The apparatus shown can be used to compare the reactivity of different metals.

    (a) What is the name of substance **X**, used to supply oxygen on heating?
    (b) How can this experiment be used to compare the reactivity of different metals?

3. When sodium metal is added to cold water, the metal melts to form the shape of a ball and quickly moves about the surface of the water. Hydrogen gas is rapidly produced and sodium hydroxide solution is formed.
    (a) How can the gas be identified?
    (b) Explain why the metal melts.
    (c) Name a metal which reacts more vigorously than sodium with water.

4. The earliest people on earth used gold and silver for making jewellery. Other metals like sodium and magnesium were unknown until approximately 200 years ago.
    (a) Explain why gold and silver were among the first metals to be discovered.
    (b) Explain why sodium and magnesium were **not** discovered until recent times.

5. Some metals are found **uncombined** in the earth's crust but most have to be extracted from their **ores**.
    (a) Explain what is meant by each of the terms in **bold**?
    (b) Name **two** metals which are found uncombined.
    (c) What can be concluded about the reactivity of metals which are found uncombined?
    (d) Name a metal that can be extracted from its ore by heating with carbon.

6. A pupil carried out some experiments with iron oxide, sodium oxide and silver oxide. On heating the three metal oxides, it was found that one decomposed to form the metal and oxygen gas. On heating with carbon, one of the other two metal oxides reacted to form the metal.

   (a) Which metal oxide would decompose on heating alone?
   (b) Which metal oxide would **not** decompose on heating with carbon?

7. Iron is produced from ore by a process called smelting. The chemical reactions take place in a huge tower.

   (a) What name is given to the tower?
   (b) The following reactions take place in the tower.
       Write a word equation for each.
       (i)   the burning of the coke
       (ii) the production of carbon monoxide gas
       (iii) the formation of iron from the ore

8. The oxides of metals **X** and **Y** are unaffected by heat but the oxide of **Z** gives off oxygen when it is heated. The oxide of **Y** is stable to heating with carbon but the oxide of **X** decomposes.

   (a) Place the three metals in order of reactivity. (Start with the most reactive.)
   (b) Suggest a name for each of the metals **X, Y** and **Z**.

9. A pupil was asked to investigate three metal oxides **LO, M$_2$O** and **NO**. On heating strongly, **LO** broke down into a metal **L** and oxygen. The other two oxides did not break down.

   (a) From this evidence what can be deduced about the reactivity of metal **L**?
   (b) How could you test **M$_2$O** and **NO** in order to find out which was the more reactive of the metals **M** and **N**?

10. Carbon monoxide can be used to extract iron from iron(III) oxide. Carbon dioxide is produced in the reaction.

   (a) Name the type of reaction which takes place.
   (b) Explain why calcium cannot be extracted from its oxide in this way.

11. Uranium metal is obtained from ores containing uranium(IV) oxide and uranium (VI) oxide. The extraction of the metal involves three steps.

1. The oxide is converted to uranium(VI) fluoride.

2. The uranium(VI) fluoride is reduced by hydrogen.

$$UF_6(g) + H_2(g) \xrightarrow{100\,°C} UF_4(s) + 2HF(g)$$

3. The uranium(IV) fluoride is reduced by magnesium metal.

$$UF_4(g) + 2Mg(s) \xrightarrow{1600\,°C} U(l) + 2MgF_2(l)$$

Using the information above

(a) state **two** facts that can be concluded about the melting point of uranium(IV) fluoride,

(b) state whether uranium is a more active or less active metal than magnesium.

12. The results of experiments with four metals **W, X, Y** and **Z** and their compounds are summarised in the table below.

Metal	Column 1 Reaction of metal with dilute acid	Column 2 Action of heat on metal oxide	Column 3 Reaction of metal with cold water
W	hydrogen evolved	no reaction	hydrogen formed
X	no reaction	no reaction	no reaction
Y	hydrogen evolved	no reaction	very slow reaction
Z	no reaction	metal formed	no reaction

(a) State what information about the order of reactivity of the metals can be obtained from

(i) Column 1 alone,

(ii) Column 2 alone.

(b) Now use **all** the information to put the metals into an order of reactivity placing the most active first.

(c) Suggest a name for each metal **W, X, Y** and **Z**.

13. **A, B, C** and **D** are four metals to be arranged in an order of reactivity.

(a) In each of the cases (i) to (iv) state which of the two metals is more reactive.

(i) The oxide of **C** does **not** decompose on heating, while that of **A** does.

(ii) **B** reacts with dilute acid to produce hydrogen gas; **D** does **not**.

(iii) When **D** is added to a solution containing ions of the metal **A**, **A** is displaced and **D** dissolves.

(iv) **C** reacts readily with cold water, **B** reacts slowly with steam.

(b) Use the above information to place the four metals in order of reactivity. (Start with the most reactive.)

14. Information about the metals **M**, **E**, **T**, **A** and **L** and some of their compounds is listed below.

   (i) With water, **A** reacts vigorously, **M** slowly, **E**, **T** and **L** do **not** react.

   (ii) **T** displaces **E** from a solution containing ions of **E**.

   (iii) Carbon reduces the oxides of **E** and **T** but **not** the other oxides.

   (iv) **M**, **A** and **L** react with dilute hydrochloric acid while **T** and **E** do **not**.

   (a) For each bit of information (i) to (iv), what can be concluded about the relative reactivity of the metals?

   (b) Use the above information to place the five metals in order of reactivity (most reactive first).

   (c) When nitrates of these metals are heated only one decomposes to give the metal. Which is most likely to do so?

15. Over 60 different metals occur in the earth and we have found uses for almost all of them.

   Gold has been known since the earliest civilisation. It is too soft to make into tools but is used to make jewellery and coins.

   Copper was discovered about 4000 BC. It is one of the best conductors of electricity, which makes it a good choice for electrical wiring. Its lack of reactivity makes it a good choice for making hot or cold water pipes.

   About 1000 BC, iron was first extracted from its ores. Its hardness makes it very useful, and when converted to steel it is the raw material for cars, ships, railway lines and machinery.

   The first of the modern metals to be discovered was aluminium, in 1825. This light metal does not corrode to a large extent. Aircraft, window frames, milk bottle tops and wrapping foil are all made from aluminium.

   Present the above information in a table with **four** headings.

16. Steel is an alloy of iron and carbon. The table shows how two properties of steel change as the percentage of carbon is increased.

Percentage of carbon	Hardness	Strength
0.00 - 0.15	low	high
0.16 - 0.25	medium	high
0.26 - 0.50	high	medium
0.51 - 1.50	high	low

   (a) State how the hardness of steel changes as the percentage of carbon is increased.

   (b) Predict the **two** properties of a steel containing 1.7% carbon.

17. Solders are alloys of lead (melting point 327 °C) and tin (melting point 232 °C). The table shows the melting points of solders containing different proportions of tin.

Percentage of tin in solder (by mass)	Melting point / °C
10	305
20	280
30	260
40	240
50	215
60	190
70	190
80	200
90	215

(a) Draw a **line graph** of melting point against percentage of tin in solders.

(b) State the percentage of lead present in the solder with the lowest melting point.

(c) Solders which do not contain lead are made. They are used to solder pipes for drinking water.

Suggest why this has been done.

18. Caesium can be produced by heating a mixture of calcium and caesium chloride to 750 °C.

$$Ca + 2CsCl \rightarrow CaCl_2 + 2Cs$$

(a) State whether caesium would be formed as a solid, liquid or gas in this reaction.

(You may wish to use page 3 of the data booklet to help you.)

(b) Caesium must be stored in the absence of water and air.

Suggest a reason for this.

19. Read the following passage.

"Magnesium reacts readily with acids and oxygen.

Aluminium might be expected to behave in a similar way. However, if you test aluminium, you will often find that this is not the case. This is mainly due to a layer of aluminium oxide forming very rapidly when the metal is first exposed to air.

This oxide layer does not flake off or allow air and water to pass through it. It is this layer which prevents further corrosion of the aluminium."

Which of the following would be the most suitable title for the passage?

    A   Reactions of metals   **B**   Reactions with air

    C   The oxidation of metals   **D**   The reactivity of aluminium.

20. Consider the following statements about the reactions between selected metals and air.

"Nickel is relatively inert to corrosion at ordinary temperatures. It burns, producing its oxide (NiO), when roasted in air.

Cobalt is not affected by air at room temperature. However, when the temperature is raised, it forms a surface layer of oxide.

Strong heating of manganese brings about the following reaction, which does **not** occur under normal conditions.

$$3Mn(s) + 2O_2(g) \rightarrow Mn_3O_4(s)$$

Chromium burns well only at temperatures well over 2000 K. Below this temperature it is unreactive."

Use the information to write out **two** general statements which could be applied to **all** of the four metals.

21. Some magnesium ribbon was added to dilute hydrochloric acid in a test tube. Bubbles of gas were given off, quite slowly at first, but more quickly after a few seconds. The contents of the test tube became warmer.

The following five statements are all true.

A   During the reaction, acid is used up, so fewer $H^+(aq)$ ions are left.

B   Reactions speed up when the temperature increases.

C   The magnesium has a thin oxide layer which first reacts with the acid.

D   Magnesium reacts slowly with water as well as with acid.

E   Magnesium reacts more quickly with acid than do most other metals.

Which **two** statements can be used to explain why the bubbles of gas were given off more quickly after a few seconds than at the very start of the reaction.

22. Nuclear reactors can overheat and become very dangerous.
Liquid sodium can be used to cool down reactors. It flows round the reactor in pipes.

(a) Suggest why sodium is used rather than iron.
You may wish to use the data booklet to help you.

(b) Suggest why sodium is used rather than water.

Exercise 3.11

1. Each year corrosion costs our country millions of pounds.
    (a) Explain what is meant by corrosion.
    (b) What special term is applied to the corrosion of iron?
    (c) Consider this list of substances:

    glass, magnesium, sandstone, sulphur, zinc,
    calcium carbonate, sodium, aluminium, plastic, calcium

    Copy the table and place each of the substances in the appropriate column.

Substances which corrode	Substances which do not corrode

2. (a) Apart from iron, what **two** substances are necessary for rusting to occur?
    (b) When iron rusts, what happens to the iron atoms?

3. Acid rain is common in industrial areas.
    How does acid rain affect the rate of corrosion of metals?

4. Three test tubes were set up as shown.

A - iron nail   B - iron nail   C - iron nail
in salt water   in water   in glucose solution

Ferroxyl indicator was added to each of the tubes. On inspection it was found that the nail in tube **A** had corroded most. The amount of corrosion in tubes **B** and **C** was much the same.
    (a) How does ferroxyl indicator help to compare the rates of corrosion?
    (b) Explain why salt in the water speeds up the rate of corrosion whereas glucose does not.

5.   A pupil set up the following experiment.

A   B   C

     tin   iron   iron   iron   magnesium

(a)   In which experiment would the corrosion of iron be fastest?

(b)   Explain your answer.

6.   Explain each of the following.

(a)   A ship corrodes faster at sea than on a fresh-water loch.

(b)   The hulls of ships often have blocks of magnesium attached to them.

(c)   It is inadvisable for a plumber to attach copper piping to an iron storage tank.

(d)   Iron railings which are painted corrode less rapidly than unpainted railings.

(e)   It is inadvisable for a plumber to use solder containing lead to join copper pipes.

(f)   A motor car body is often connected to the negative terminal of the car battery.

(g)   Scrap magnesium can be used to protect underground storage tanks but scrap copper **cannot** be used.

7.   The experiment shown was carried out to investigate the rusting of iron.

solution gradually   water containing   solution did not
turned blue   an indicator   change colour

iron   galvanised
                                                      iron

(a)   Suggest a name for the indicator used.

(b)   Explain what is meant by **galvanised** iron.

(c)   Why does galvanised iron hardly rust even when badly scratched?

8.   Both zinc and tin are used to protect iron and steel containers from corrosion.

Metal dustbins are made from iron which has been dipped into molten zinc; cans for food are tin-plated.

(a)   What name is given to the process of coating iron with zinc?

(b)   Explain why zinc is preferred to tin for protecting dustbins.

9. Two corrosion experiments with iron nails are shown.

Experiment 1   Experiment 2

(a) In experiment 1, which nail, **A** or **B**, will be protected against rusting?

(b) In experiment 2, how does the magnesium protect the nail from rusting?

(c) For each of these experiments describe how the method is actually used to protect iron or steel on a large scale.

10. Oil rigs, made of iron and steel, corrode readily at sea.

State **one** method which could be used to help prevent corrosion of oil rigs and explain briefly how the method works.

11. Galvanising could be said to provide 'double protection' against corrosion of iron.

This is because the process provides both physical protection and electrochemical protection.

Explain whether or not a coating of copper instead of zinc would be as effective in providing

(a) physical protection,

(b) electrochemical protection.

12. **X** and **Y** are two metals. When each is attached to iron only **Y** decreases the speed of rusting of iron.

(a) Which metal is more reactive, **X** or **Y**?

(b) Which metal would be most effective in sacrificially protecting iron?

13. Both silver and gold are used to cover objects made of steel. As well as providing an attractive finish, the steel is protected against corrosion.

(a) What name is given to the process of coating steel with silver or gold?

(b) Explain why the coating protects the iron against corrosion.

14. Equipment used by Scott in his expedition to the South Pole nearly eighty years ago has been found recently. It shows very little sign of rusting.

Explain why iron rusts so slowly when the temperature is below 0 °C.

15. Steel can be protected from rusting by coating it with other substances.
One method is dipping it in molten plastic.
    (a) Why does coating steel with plastic prevent rusting?
    (b) Chromium plated steel rusts quickly if scratched.
        What does this tell you about the reactivity of chromium?

16. Corrosion involves atoms at the surface of a metal losing electrons and changing
to metal ions.
    (a) State the name of this kind of reaction.
    (b) Write ion-electron equations to show what happens to the metal atoms
        during the corrosion of
        (i) iron,   (ii) zinc,
        (iii) magnesium,   (iv) aluminium.
    (c) Write the ion-electron equation to show what can happen to the iron(II) ions
        which are formed during the corrosion of iron.
    (d) Write the ion-electron equation to show how hydroxide ions are formed
        during corrosion of a metal.

17. Two experiments are set up as shown.

Explain why the nail in experiment **B** did not rust.

18. Acid mists lead to faster corrosion of metals.
    (a) Write ion-electron equations for each of the reactions which occur when
        iron is corroded by acid.
    (b) Explain why galvanising does **not** protect iron permanently from corrosion
        by acid.

19. Three experiments were set up outside to investigate the corrosion of "tin" cans. These cans are made of iron which has been coated with tin.

(a) (i) In which experiment will the iron **not** rust?

(ii) Explain your answer.

(b) (i) In which experiment will the iron rust fastest?

(ii) Explain your answer.

20. Consider the following cells.

gel containing ferroxyl indicator plus an electrolyte

(a) Name the ion which reacts with ferroxyl indicator to produce

(i) a blue colour,

(ii) a red colour.

(b) What colour, if any, will be observed at each of the electrodes in the three cells?

(c) Write the ion-electron equation to show the reaction at each electrode in the three cells.

(d) What is the direction of electron flow in each of the cells?

21. Archaeologists found some corroded silver coins and a badly rusted sword.
    (a) The silver coins were restored by wrapping them in zinc foil in a beaker of salt solution.
        What type of reaction took place?
    (b) The iron blade was attached to its handle by a copper band.
        Explain why, although the copper was uncorroded, the iron had rusted badly.

22. Dental amalgam is a mixture of metals including mercury, silver and tin. The amalgam slowly corrodes in the mouth. Corrosion is more rapid if the amalgam makes contact with a gold filling in a neighbouring tooth.
    Explain why contact with gold increases the rate of corrosion of the dental amalgam.

23. In the 19th century, Humphrey Davy suggested that the Royal Navy could protect the copper sheeting on the hulls of its ships from corrosion by attaching small patches of iron to them.
    (a) Write the ion-electron equation to show what happens to the atoms when copper corrodes.
    (b) Explain why attaching patches of iron would have prevented the copper from corroding.

24. "OLD COPPER BOTTOM"

    "Old Copper Bottom" was the nickname of William Forbes of Stirling, who lived during the 18th century.

    Forbes made his fortune by buying up all the available copper in the country when he heard rumours that the Navy was planning to experiment with copper sheeting on the hulls of its wooden warships. He sold the copper to the Navy at a large profit and when the experiment failed because of the use of iron nails, he bought the copper back at a lower price.

    Forbes then pointed out the obvious fact that copper nails should have been used. After this he was able to resell the copper to the Admiralty, and made a second large profit.

    Explain why it is "obvious" that copper nails and **not** iron nails should have been used in the experiment.

Prescribed Practical Activities

1. Dilute hydrochloric acid reacts with sodium thiosulphate solution producing sulphur.

syringe with 1 cm³ acid

20 cm³ sodium thiosulphate solution

card

The sulphur produced slowly obscures the cross on the card beneath the beaker.

You are given

> sodium thiosulphate solution,
>
> hydrochloric acid,
>
> any laboratory equipment you require.

Describe fully how you would investigate the effect of temperature on the rate of the reaction between sodium thiosulphate and hydrochloric acid.

2. Part of a workcard is shown.

WORKCARD

To find the effect of varying the concentration of sodium persulphate solution on the rate of its reaction with potassium iodide solution:

Experiment	1	2	3	4
Volume of sodium persulphate solution / cm³	10	8	6	4
Volume of water / cm³	0			
Volume of potassium iodide solution / cm³	10			

(a) What volumes of water are used in Experiments 2, 3 and 4?

(b) What is used to indicate the end of the reaction?

3. A pupil was investigating the effect of temperature on the rate of a reaction. A reaction which produces sulphur from dilute hydrochloric acid and sodium thiosulphate solution was used.

This is what was done.

1. The following solutions were measured out.

20 cm³ sodium thiosulphate solution

2. The beaker was heated in a water bath to approximately 30 °C.

3. The beaker was then placed on a card with an **X** on it and the exact temperature of the sodium thiosulphate solution was measured.

thermometer

paper with X mark

4. A syringe was then used to add 1 cm³ of the acid to the sodium thiosulphate solution and the time for the **X** to be obscured by the sulphur was noted.

5. The apparatus was thoroughly washed out.

6. The experiment was repeated once at a temperature of approximately 40 °C.

State **two** ways of improving the above investigation procedure.

4. The effect of concentration on the rate of a reaction can be found using potassium iodide solution with different concentrations of sodium persulphate solution in the presence of starch.

   (a) Apart from temperature, give **four** factors which must be kept constant.

   (b) What colour change is observed when the reaction has gone a set "distance"?

5. (a) Draw a labelled diagram of apparatus which could be used to identify the products formed at the electrodes during the electrolysis of copper(II) chloride solution.

   (b) How can the products at each electrode be identified?

6. (a) Describe briefly how to test a hydrocarbon for unsaturation.

   (b) Apart from wearing eye protection, give **one** safety precaution which should be taken in this experiment.

7. (a) Draw a diagram of the apparatus which could be used to crack liquid paraffin and test the products for unsaturation.

   (b) (i) Explain what is meant by "suck-back".

      (ii) What steps can be taken to prevent suck-back?

8. Starch can be hydrolysed using an enzyme or an acid.

   (a) Complete the sentence below.

      In the hydrolysis of starch using an enzyme or an acid, the enzyme and acid act as a _____.

   (b) What solution is used to detect the type of substance formed by the hydrolysis of starch?

9. Magnesium sulphate can be prepared by the reaction of magnesium or magnesium carbonate with dilute sulphuric acid.

   (a) Name each of **three** steps involved in the preparation.

   (b) Why as an excess of magnesium or magnesium carbonate used in the first step?

10. Two students were investigating a factor which might affect the size of the voltage generated by a simple cell.
    Bill was investigating the effect of using different metals; Mary was investigating the effect of using different electrolytes.

    (a) Draw a labelled diagram of the apparatus which both could have used in their first experiment.

    (b) State **three** other factors which might affect the size of the voltage generated by a single cell.

11. Zinc, copper and magnesium can be placed in order of reactivity by their reactions with oxygen.
    (a) Draw a labelled diagram of the apparatus which could be used.
    (b) (i) Clearly label the point of heating at the start and describe how this changes with time.
        (ii) Explain your answer.
    (c) What is used to give a guide to the ease with which these metals react with oxygen.
    (d) Apart from wearing eye protection, describe **three** precautions which should be taken for this particular experiment and give a reason for each.

12. The apparatus below can be used to show that the hydrolysis of starch is affected by a catalyst.

Test tube A
starch solution

Test tube B
starch solution
+ catalyst

water

    (a) What is the purpose of test tube **A**?
    (b) (i) Name a type of substance which can catalyse the hydrolysis of starch.
        (ii) What should be the temperature of the water bath for this catalyst?
    (c) Benedict's solution is used to test for a product of the hydrolysis of starch.
        What colour change is observed when the test is positive?